REVISE GCSE
Mathematics
PRACTICE PAPERS
Foundation

THE REVISE SERIES
Available in print or online

Online editions for all titles in the Revise series are available from Autumn 2013.

Presented on our ActiveLearn platform, you can view the full book and customise it by adding notes, comments and weblinks.

Print editions

Revise GCSE Mathematics Practice Papers Foundation 9781447949916

Revise GCSE Mathematics Practice Papers Higher 9781447949886

Online editions

Revise GCSE Mathematics Practice Papers Foundation – ActiveBook 9781447949930

Revise GCSE Mathematics Practice Papers Higher – ActiveBook 9781447949909

From Autumn 2013

SOLUTION VIDEO

Worked Solution videos give step-by-step guidance on how to tackle difficult questions. They walk you through the workings, highlighting points to remember and common misconceptions. The videos offer one method of arriving at the correct answer – remember that there may be other valid methods as well.

To find out more visit:
www.pearsonschools.co.uk/mathspracticepapers

ALWAYS LEARNING

PEARSON

ActiveBook online edition

Revision is more than just this book!

Prepare for your exams with Worked Solution videos! These are available on the ActiveBook online edition – more information at:
www.pearsonschools.co.uk/mathspracticepapers

From Autumn 2013

ActiveBook is the online edition of this book: easy to use and easy to read.

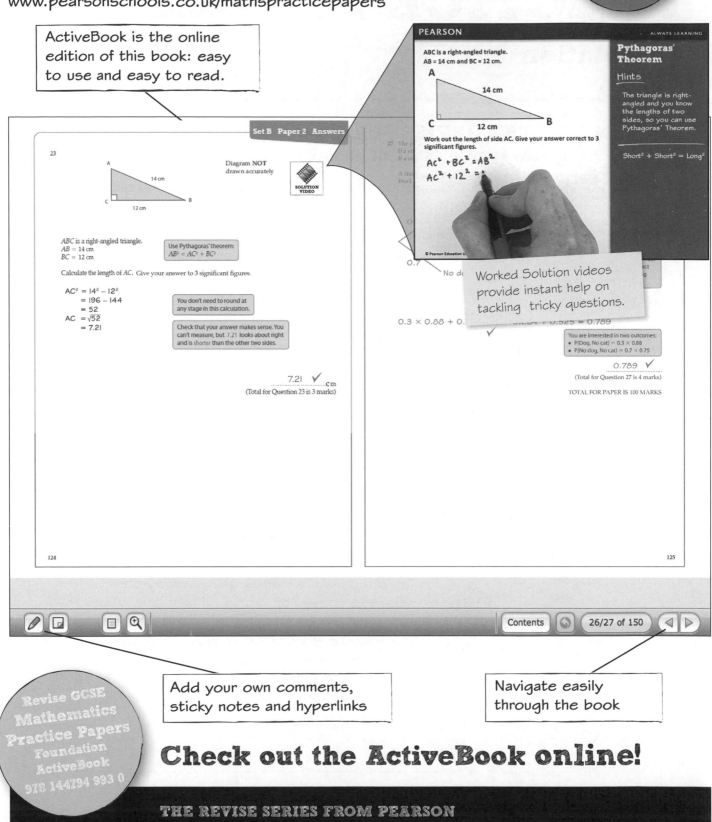

Worked Solution videos provide instant help on tackling tricky questions.

Add your own comments, sticky notes and hyperlinks

Navigate easily through the book

Check out the ActiveBook online!

Contents

QUESTION PAPERS

SET A
2   Paper 1 (non-calculator)
26   Paper 2 (calculator)

SET B
46   Paper 1 (non calculator)
66   Paper 2 (calculator)

SET C
86   Paper 1 (non-calculator)
106 Paper 2 (calculator)

ANSWERS

SET A
127 Paper 1 (non-calculator)
133 Paper 2 (calculator)

SET B
138 Paper 1 (non-calculator)
143 Paper 2 (calculator)

SET C
148 Paper 1 (non-calculator)
153 Paper 2 (calculator)

Revise GCSE Mathematics Practice Papers are designed to complement your classroom and home learning, and to help prepare you for the exam. They do not include all the content and skills needed for the complete course.

A small bit of small print

Awarding Organisations publish Sample Assessment Material and the Specifications on their websites. This is the official content. The questions in this book have been written to help you practise what you have learned in your revision. Remember: the real exam questions may not look like this.

1 (a)

Write down the number marked by the arrow.

....
(1)

(b)

Find the number 370 on the number line above.

Mark the number with an arrow (↑).

(1)

(c)

Write down the number marked by the arrow.

....
(2)
(Total for Question 1 is 4 marks)

2 Garcia and Nakti visited a fish shop and got this bill.

FRESH FRY

Cod & 2 portions of chips	£5.75
4 sausages	£5.16
Cod & chips	£4.80

Garcia paid using a £20 note.

(a) How much change did he receive?

£ ....
(3)

(b) What is the cost of one sausage?

£ ....
(2)
(Total for Question 2 is 5 marks)

3   Here are the first five terms of a sequence.

$$7 \qquad 12 \qquad 17 \qquad 22 \qquad 27$$

(a) Write down the next term in the sequence.

....

(1)

Here are some terms of another sequence.

$$32 \qquad 16 \qquad 8 \qquad \ldots \qquad 2$$

(b) Write down the missing term in this sequence.

....

(1)

(Total for Question 3 is 2 marks)

*4   The table shows the types of television set in the houses of a street.

Year	Analogue TV	Digital TV
2002	20	0
2004	18	1
2006	18	7
2008	15	15
2010	9	16

Draw a suitable diagram to show the information in the table.

Use the grid below.

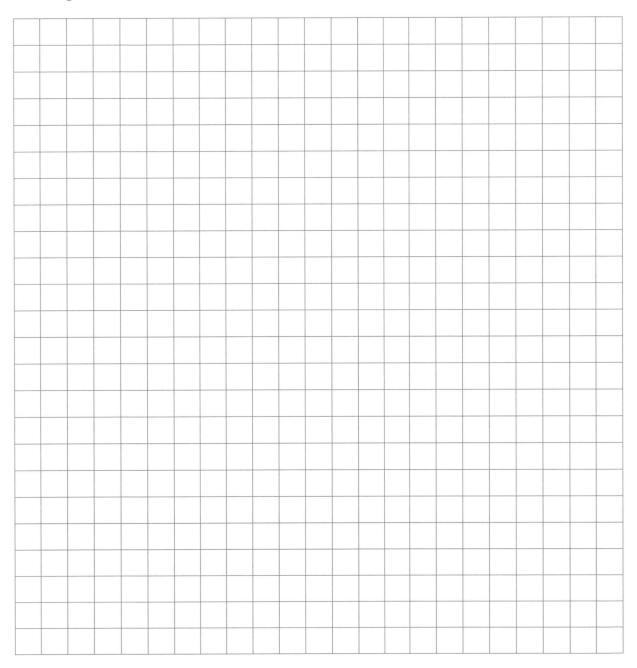

(Total for Question 4 is 4 marks)

5 Here are two rectangles.

Rectangle **A** is drawn on a grid of centimetre squares.

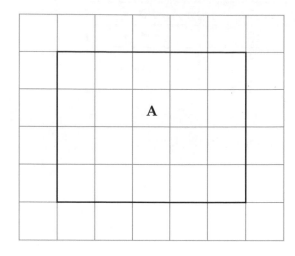 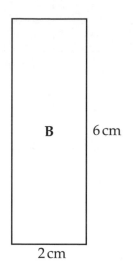

(a) Find the area of rectangle **A**.

.... cm²

(1)

*(b) Which of the two rectangles has the greater perimeter?

(3)

(Total for Question 5 is 4 marks)

6   The pictogram shows the money collected by Year 10 for three different charities.

Oxfam	◯◯◯◯
The Red Cross	◯◯
Save the Children	◯◯◺
Water Aid	

Key: ◯ represents £20

(a)   Write down the amount collected for Oxfam.

£.................................
(1)

(b)   How much more money was collected for Save the Children than for the Red Cross?

£.................................
(1)

£50 was collected for Water Aid.

(c)   Use this information to complete the pictogram.

(1)
(Total for Question 6 is 3 marks)

7   The diagram shows an arrow that can rotate around the points of a compass.

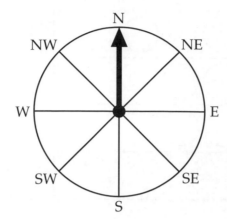

The angle rotates clockwise from N to E.

(a)   (i) Write down the angle the arrow turns.

....................................°

(1)

(ii) Write down the special name for this angle.

....

(1)

The arrow rotates clockwise from W to E in three equal steps.

(b)   Work out the angle the arrow turns in each step.

....................................°

(2)

(Total for Question 7 is 4 marks)

8   (a)   Write down 80% as a fraction in its simplest form.

....
                                                                        (2)

(b)   Which is the larger, $\dfrac{5}{6}$ or 75%?

You must show all your working.

....
                                                                        (2)
(Total for Question 8 is 4 marks)

9   Simon had c coins in his coin box.
    He put 5 more coins into the coin box.

    (a)   Write down an expression, in terms of c, for the number of coins now in the box.

....
                                                                        (1)

    Tara bought e eggs.
    She used n eggs to make an omelette.

    (b)   Write down an expression, in terms of e and n, for the number of eggs Tara has left.

....
                                                                        (1)
(Total for Question 9 is 2 marks)

10

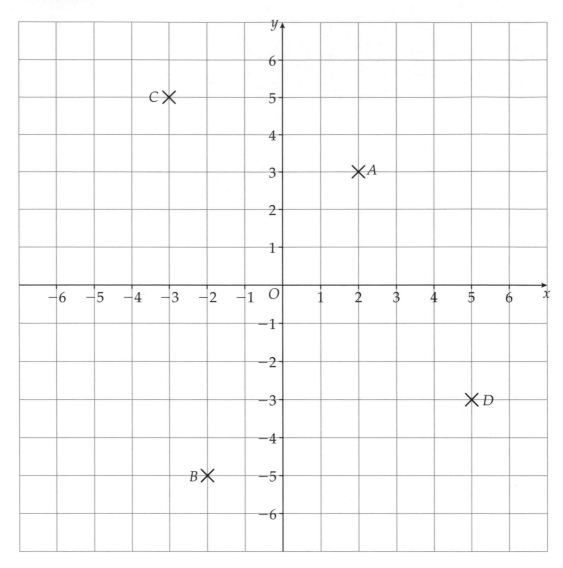

(a) Write down the letter of the point with coordinates $(-3, 5)$.

....

(1)

(b) Write down the coordinates of the point A.

(................ , ...)

(1)

(c) Join the points A and B with a straight line.
Mark the midpoint of your line with a cross ($\times$).

(1)

(Total for Question 10 is 3 marks)

11 Here are the winning numbers in a lottery game.

    6   9   21   27   31   39

   (a) Which number is a prime number?

   ....
                                                                  (1)

   (b) Which number is a multiple of one of the other numbers?

   ....
                                                                  (1)

   (c) Which number is a square number?

   ....
                                                                  (1)
                                    (Total for Question 11 is 3 marks)

12 (a) Write down the value of $\sqrt{64}$

   ....
                                                                  (1)

   (b) Work out $5 \times (2 + 7)$

   ....
                                                                  (1)
                                    (Total for Question 12 is 2 marks)

13   (a)   Draw all the lines of symmetry on this shape.

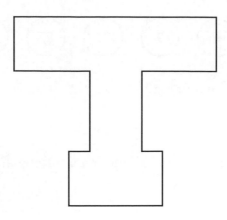

(1)

(b)   Add **one** line to this shape to give it rotational symmetry of order 2

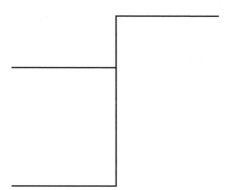

(1)

(Total for Question 13 is 2 marks)

14   Here is part of a train timetable from Filton to Freshford.

Filton to Freshford

Filton	10 26	11 23	12 26	14 26	15 23
Bristol	10 49	11 49	12 39	14 48	15 44
Oldfield Park	11 03	11 56	12 53	15 02	15 58
Bath	11 07	12 07	12 57	15 06	16 02
Freshford	11 16	12 16	13 06	15 15	16 11

A train goes from Filton to Bath.
This train leaves Filton at 10 26

(a)   Work out how many minutes the train takes to go from Filton to Bath.

....
(1)

Marcus arrives at Filton station at 10 30

(b)   What is the earliest time Marcus can now arrive in Bristol?

....
(1)

Fiona arrives at Bristol station at 12 39

She visits a shopping mall in Bristol.
It takes 10 minutes to walk between the station and the shopping mall.
She wants to spend as long as possible in the shopping mall.

Fiona has arranged to meet a friend at Freshford station at 4.11 pm.

(c)   How long can Fiona spend in the shopping mall?

....
(2)
(Total for Question 14 is 4 marks)

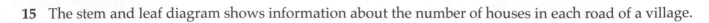

15 The stem and leaf diagram shows information about the number of houses in each road of a village.

```
0 | 8  8
1 | 4  4  7  9
2 | 0  0  6  8  8  8  9
3 | 0  2  2  5  5
4 | 6
```

Key:
3 | 2 represents 32 houses

(a) How many roads are there in the village?

....

(1)

(b) Work out the median number of houses.

....

(1)

(c) Work out the range.

....

(2)

(Total for Question 15 is 4 marks)

16 (a) Simplify $e + e + e + e + e + e + e$

....
(1)

(b) Simplify $2p + 3q + 4p + q$

....
(2)

(c) Expand $3(m + 2n)$

....
(1)

(Total for Question 16 is 4 marks)

17 (a) Solve $t + 8 = 3$

$t = $ ....
(1)

(b) Solve $3w = 24$

$w = $ ....
(1)

(c) Solve $4h + 5 = 13$

$h = $ ....
(2)

(Total for Question 17 is 4 marks)

18 Josh asked the students in his class about the sports they liked most.
The pie chart below shows the results.

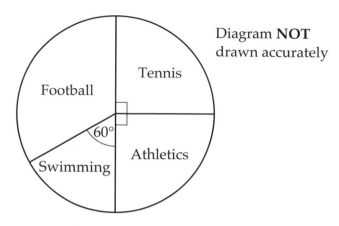

Diagram **NOT**
drawn accurately

6 students liked athletics most.

How many liked football most?

....

(Total for Question 18 is 3 marks)

19 (a) Write down 1 000 000 as a power of 10

....

(1)

(b) Work out $4^2 + 3^3$

....

(2)

(Total for Question 19 is 3 marks)

20   The graph shows a cycle journey made by Jiao to pick up a dress from a shop.

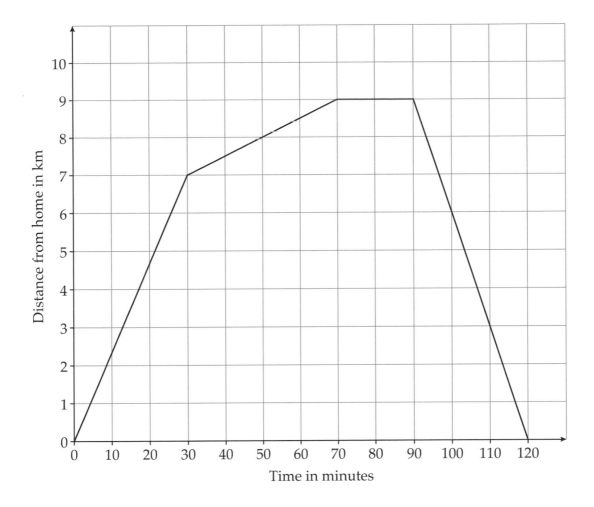

Jiao cycled from home to the park where she met her friend.
They cycled to the dress shop.
Jiao tried on the dress then cycled back home.

(a)   How far is the park from Jiao's home?

.... km

(1)

(b)   How long did Jiao spend in the dress shop?

.... minutes

(1)

(c)   Work out Jiao's speed on her return journey.

.... km/h

(2)

(Total for Question 20 is 4 marks)

21   The diagram shows a solid block of wood in the shape of a cuboid.

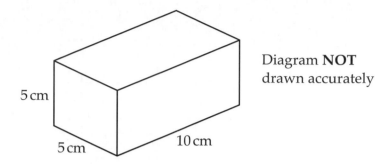

Diagram **NOT** drawn accurately

5 cm

5 cm   10 cm

(a)   Work out the total surface area of the cuboid.

.... cm²

(1)

Karl has to paint all 6 faces of 50 cuboids.

A can of spray paint covers an area of 3000 cm².

(b)   How many cans of paint must Karl buy to paint all the faces?
       Show all of your working.

....

(3)

(Total for Question 21 is 4 marks)

22 Tania and Sebastian receive £60 from their parents.

They share the money in the same ratio as their ages.
Tania is 10 and Sebastian is 14

(a) Write the ratio of their ages Tania : Sebastian in its simplest form.

....

(1)

(b) Work out how much money Sebastian got.

£ ....

(2)

(Total for Question 22 is 3 marks)

23 (a) Write the number 2.7098 correct to 3 decimal places.

....

(1)

(b) Given that $\dfrac{35 \times 5.4}{42} = 4.5$

work out the value of $\dfrac{350 \times 54}{4.2}$

....

(2)

(Total for Question 23 is 3 marks)

*24 The table below shows details of two companies offering 18-month mobile phone contracts.

Company	Monthly charge	Picture messaging
M-Link	First 6 months FREE, then £25 per month	15p each
Air Talk	£20 per month	FREE

Michelle wants to sign up for an 18-month contract.

She sends 20 picture messages each month.

Michelle wants to pay the least amount of money for her contract.

Which company contract would you advise Michelle to sign up to?
You must show all your working.

(Total for Question 24 is 4 marks)

25 The scatter graph shows information about some machinists making jeans.
It shows the number of months each machinist has been working and the number of errors they made during the last month.

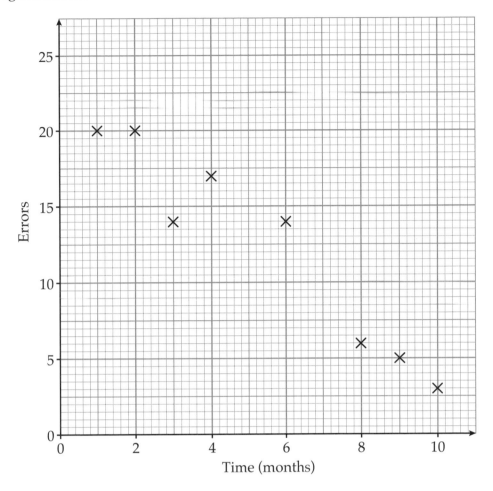

(a) What type of correlation does the scatter graph show?

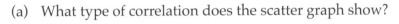

(1)

A machinist who had been working for 7 months was also checked.

(b) Estimate the number of errors he made during the last month.

....

(2)

(Total for Question 25 is 3 marks)

26 Here is the recipe Jackie uses for glazing her pots.

> 210 ml red
> 450 ml light yellow
> 360 ml dark yellow
> 480 ml white

(a) What volume of glazing does this recipe make?

.... ml

(1)

Jackie needs to make only 1 litre of the glazing.

(b) How much of each colour will she need?

.... ml red

.... ml light yellow

.... ml dark yellow

.... ml white

(3)

(Total for Question 26 is 4 marks)

*27

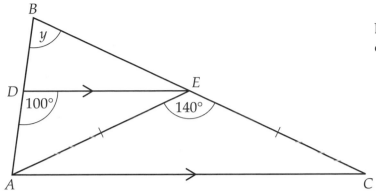

Diagram **NOT**
drawn accurately

ABC is a triangle.
DE is parallel to *AC*.

Angle *AEC* = 140°.
Angle *ADE* = 100°.
AE = *EC*.

Work out the value of *y*.
Give reasons for your answer.

(Total for Question 27 is 5 marks)

28 Joel is conducting a survey to find out how many cans of fizzy drink his friends drink.
He decides to use a questionnaire.

Write down a suitable question he could use in his survey.

(Total for Question 28 is 3 marks)

29 Here is a diagram of a parallelogram and a rectangle.

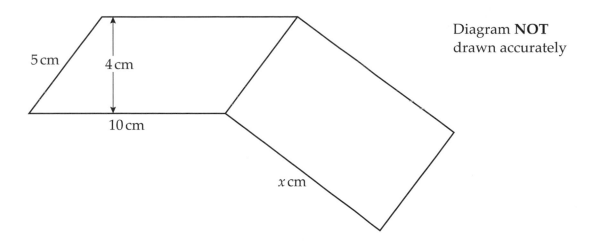

Diagram **NOT**
drawn accurately

The parallelogram has the same area as the rectangle.

Work out the length x.

.... cm
(Total for Question 29 is 3 marks)

TOTAL FOR PAPER IS 100 MARKS

1   (a)   Write down the number **seven thousand and thirty-two** in figures.

....
   (1)

(b)   Write down the value of the digit **7** in the number 27 206

....
   (1)

(c)   Write 2453 to the nearest hundred.

....
   (1)
(Total for Question 1 is 3 marks)

2   $M = 5a - b$

$a = 7.7$
$b = 5.3$

Work out the value of M.

....
(Total for Question 2 is 2 marks)

3   The composite bar chart shows the time, in minutes, Clara and Freddie spent on their homework.

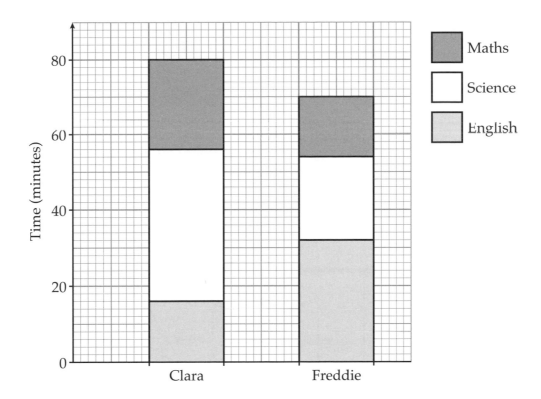

Clara said she spent a greater total time on Maths and English than Freddie.

Is Clara right?
Show all of your working.

....

(Total for Question 3 is 2 marks)

4 (a) Simplify $2a + 5a$

....
(1)

(b) Simplify $4b - b$

....
(1)

(c) Simplify $3c + 2c - 4c$

....
(1)
(Total for Question 4 is 3 marks)

5
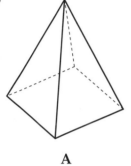 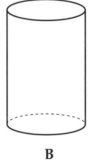 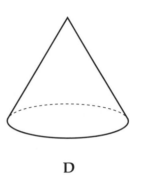 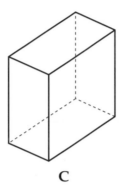 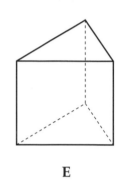

  A   **B**   **C**   **D**   **E**

(a) Write down the letter of the shape that is a cone.

....
(1)

(b) How many vertices does shape **C** have?

....
(1)

(c) Write down the mathematical name of shape **E**.

....
(1)
(Total for Question 5 is 3 marks)

6   This diagram is drawn accurately.

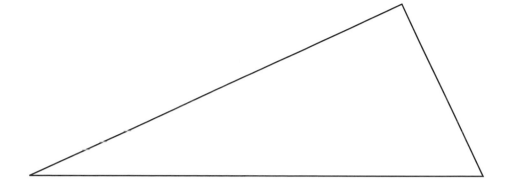

The vertices of this triangle are A, B and C.

Angle A = 65°.
Angle B = 90°.
Angle C = 25°.

Mark the vertices A, B and C and the angles on the diagram.

(Total for Question 6 is 2 marks)

*7   At a fairground, it costs £2.50 to ride in a dodgem car.
One or two people can ride in each dodgem car.

Darren, Yolanda and Upendra want at least 3 rides each on the dodgem cars.

Work out the total cheapest cost for the children.
You must show all of your working.

(Total for Question 7 is 3 marks)

8

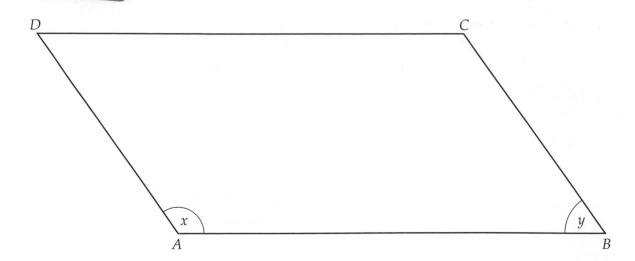

(a) Measure the length of *AB*.

....
(1)

(b) Measure the size of angle *x*.

°
....
(1)

(c) Write down the mathematical name for angle *y*.

....
(1)
(Total for Question 8 is 3 marks)

9 The table gives some information about 5 brands of printer paper.

Brand	Sheets per packet	Weight	Price per 100 sheets	Recycled	Packets per box
Eco-Paper	200	90 g	£0.76	✓	2
SuperStrong	190	100 g	£0.74	✗	8
Paper White	200	90 g	£0.64	✗	6
Copy Write	240	100 g	£0.82	✓	8
Smooth	320	90 g	£0.68	✗	8

(a) Which brand has the lowest price per 100 sheets?

....

(1)

(b) Which brand with a weight of 90 g has 8 packets per box?

....

(1)

(c) Describe **two** differences between SuperStrong and Copy Write.

1 ....

2 ....

(2)

(Total for Question 9 is 4 marks)

31

10 Sophie, Mark and Kim raced each other over a fixed distance.
    The table shows their times before and after a week of training.

	Sophie	Mark	Kim
Time before training (seconds)	62.30	85.50	58.00
Time after training (seconds)	58.75	81.20	56.25

Sophie aimed to reduce her running time by 3.5 seconds.

(a) Did Sophie achieve her goal?
     Show all of your working.

     ....

     (2)

(b) Who reduced their running time the most?
     Show all of your working.

     ....

     (3)
     (Total for Question 10 is 5 marks)

11 Zoe's colleagues gave her a £200 gift voucher for the online shop Photo Plus.

The table below shows prices for prints of photographs.

Size	Standard	Deluxe
30 cm by 20 cm	£24.99	£48.19
40 cm by 30 cm	£43.99	£55.99
61 cm by 40 cm	£51.49	£72.49
Hanging clip 85p		FREE p&p

Zoe orders the following prints:

    1 Deluxe print 40 cm by 30 cm
    2 Standard prints 30 cm by 20 cm
    1 Standard print 61 cm by 40 cm

Each print needs two hanging clips.

How much money does Zoe have left from her £200 gift voucher?

£ ....

(Total for Question 11 is 4 marks)

12

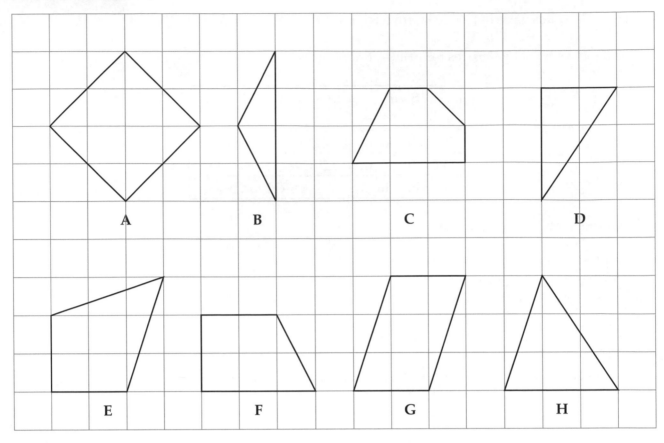

(a) Which shape is a quadrilateral with only one pair of parallel sides?

....
(1)

(b) How many lines of symmetry does shape **A** have?

....
(1)

(c) Which shape is a triangle with an obtuse angle?

....
(1)

(d) What is the order of rotational symmetry of shape **G**?

....
(1)
(Total for Question 12 is 4 marks)

13 Jayden found these coins down the back of his sofa.

10p	5p	1p	1p	10p	5p	2p	2p	2p	20p
1p	1p	10p	20p	2p	2p	1p	20p	5p	10p
5p	20p	1p	1p	20p	2p	1p	1p	20p	10p

(a) Complete the frequency table for the information in the list.

Coin value	Tally	Frequency
1p		
2p		
5p		
10p		
20p		

(2)

1p and 2p coins are copper.
5p, 10p and 20p coins are silver.

(b) Work out the difference between the total value of the copper coins and the total value of the silver coins that Jayden found.

£ ....

(3)

(Total for Question 13 is 5 marks)

14

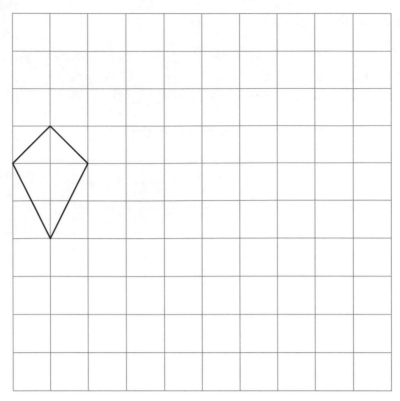

(a) What is the mathematical name of the quadrilateral drawn on the grid?

....

(1)

(b) On the grid, show how the quadrilateral tessellates.
You should draw at least 6 shapes.

(2)

(Total for Question 14 is 3 marks)

---

15 Rosario recorded the outside temperature at different times during the weekend.

Time	6 am	Noon	6 pm	Midnight
Saturday	−2 °C	8 °C	2 °C	−5 °C
Sunday	−4 °C	9 °C	0 °C	−8 °C

(a) What was the lowest recorded temperature?

.... °C

(1)

(b) When was the recorded temperature 6 °C lower than the temperature at 6 pm on Saturday?

....

(1)

(c) What is the difference between the temperature at noon on Sunday and at midnight on Saturday?

.... °C

(1)

(Total for Question 15 is 3 marks)

16 (a) Factorise $6a + 8b$

....
(1)

(b) Factorise completely $3ab - 9a^2$

....
(2)
(Total for Question 16 is 3 marks)

17 This shape is made from a rectangle and a triangle.

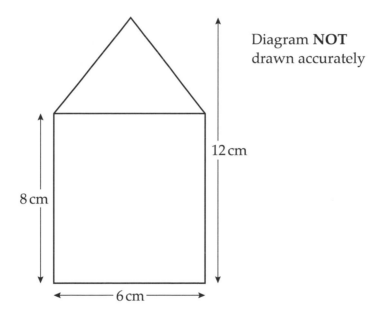

Diagram **NOT**
drawn accurately

12 cm

8 cm

6 cm

Work out the area of the shape.

.... cm²
(Total for Question 17 is 3 marks)

*18 Helen bought 36 m of climbing rope for £104.40
Jamie bought 45 m of the same type of climbing rope for £123.32

Who got the better value?
Give reasons for your answer.

(Total for Question 18 is 4 marks)

*19 Barney wants to travel from Valdosta to Atlanta in the USA.

He measures the distance between Valdosta and Atlanta on the map to be 14 cm.
The map has a scale of 1 cm to 20 miles.

His car averages 35 miles per gallon of petrol.
Petrol costs $4.59 per gallon.
His tank is empty when he sets out from Valdosta.

Barney has $25 cash in his wallet.

Will he have enough money for the journey?
Show all of your working.

(Total for Question 19 is 4 marks)

20 You can use this graph to change between gallons and litres.

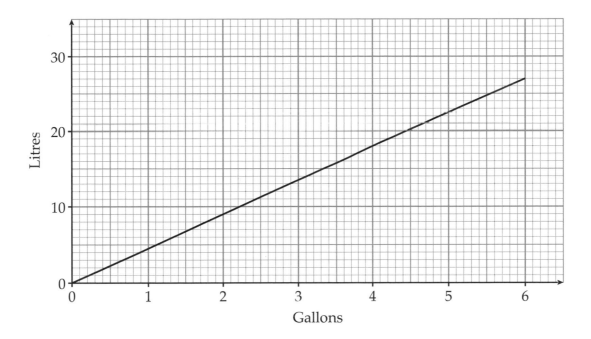

Gallons

The petrol tank of a motorcycle has a capacity of 3.6 gallons.

(a) How many litres of petrol are needed to fill the tank of the motorcycle?

.... litres

(1)

A garage is selling a 5 gallon drum of oil for the same price as a 25 litre drum of oil.

(b) Which of the drums is the better value?
    Show your working.

....

(1)

Royce filled his tractor with 10 pints of oil from a new 5 gallon drum.

1 gallon = 8 pints

(c) Estimate the number of litres of oil left in the drum.

.... litres

(2)

(Total for Question 20 is 4 marks)

21 Pete recorded these prices per kg for different cheeses.

£7.50   £11.40   £16.25   £8.35   £12.80   £15.45   £9.00   £6.45

(a) Work out the median price.

£ ....

(2)

(b) Work out the mean price.

£ ....

(2)

(c) Work out the range.

£ ....

(1)

(Total for Question 21 is 5 marks)

22 Marin placed 3 red balls and 2 blue balls inside a bag.

She asked a friend to choose one of the balls without looking.

(a) What is the probability that her friend chose a blue ball?

....
(2)

Marin wants to change the probability of choosing a blue ball to 0.2 by adding more red balls to the bag.

(b) How many red balls does she need to add to the bag?

....
(2)

(Total for Question 22 is 4 marks)

23 The exterior angle of a regular polygon is 40°.

(a) Work out the number of sides the polygon has.

....
(2)

This diagram shows a regular pentagon.

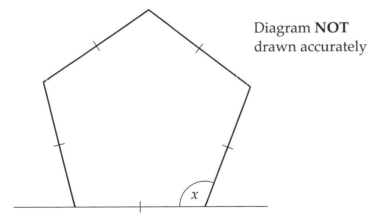

Diagram **NOT**
drawn accurately

(b) Find the size of the interior angle x.
    You must show your working.

°
....
(2)

(Total for Question 23 is 4 marks)

41

24 Use your calculator to find the value of $\dfrac{174}{6.2 - \sqrt{18}}$

Write your answer correct to 3 significant figures.

(Total for Question 24 is 3 marks)

*25 Here is a diagram of a farmer's field.

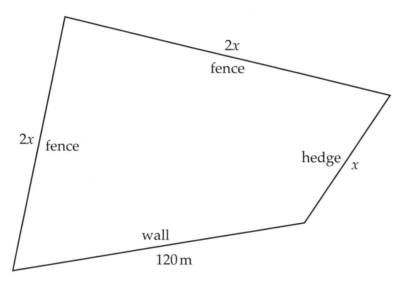

Diagram **NOT** drawn accurately

The perimeter of the field is 520 m.

The farmer wants to replace the fence with new wire.

He has 300 m of wire.
There is fencing along 2 edges.

Does the farmer have enough wire?
You must show your working.

(Total for Question 25 is 4 marks)

26 (a) The number x satisfies the inequality $3 < x \leqslant 7$

Show the inequality on the number line.

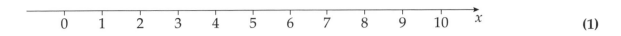

(1)

(b) (i) Solve the inequality

$$4n + 7 \geqslant 21$$

....

(2)

n is an integer.

(ii) Write down the smallest possible value of n.

....

(1)

(Total for Question 26 is 4 marks)

27

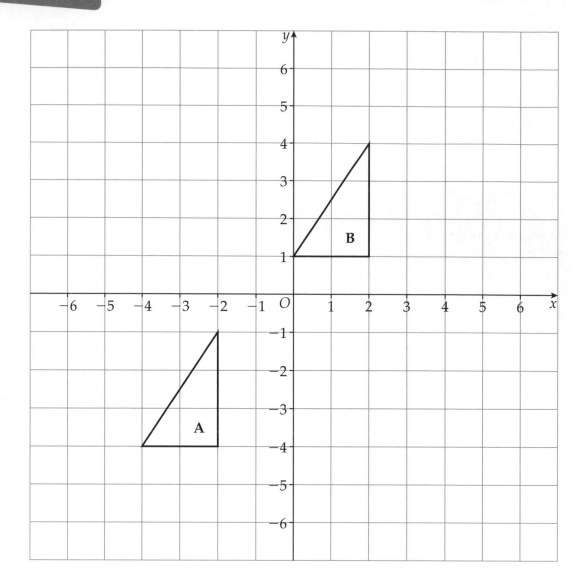

(a) Rotate triangle **A** 90° anti-clockwise about the origin.

(2)

(b) Fully describe the transformation that maps triangle **A** onto triangle **B**.

....

(2)

(Total for Question 27 is 4 marks)

28 Two shops are selling the same jacket in the January sales.

Suits You
Jacket
£140 plus VAT @ 20%

Smarts
Jacket
£180 incl. VAT
12% off marked price

In which shop is the jacket cheaper?
Show all of your working.

....
(Total for Question 28 is 5 marks)

TOTAL FOR PAPER IS 100 MARKS

1 (a) Toby measures this length of wood.

Write down the length of the wood.

.... cm

(1)

(b) Tim measures this length of metal.

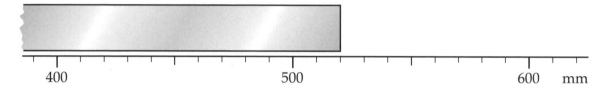

Write down the length of the metal.

.... mm

(1)

(c) Here is part of the scale on a set of weighing scales.

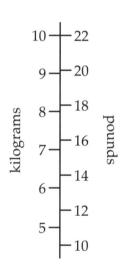

Use the scale to find an estimate for

(i) 5 kg in pounds

.... pounds

(1)

(ii) 16 pounds in kilograms.

.... kilograms

(1)

(Total for Question 1 is 4 marks)

2 (a) A shop sold 63 cans on Monday, 134 cans on Tuesday and 55 cans on Wednesday.

How many cans will the shop need to order to replace the cans sold?

....

(2)

(b) A shop has 80 bottles of perfume in stock.
The shop then sells 23 bottles of perfume.

How many bottles of perfume are now in stock?

....

(2)

(Total for Question 2 is 4 marks)

3 Write down the name of each of these 3-D solids.

(a)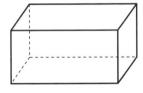

(b)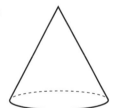

(c)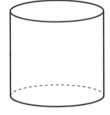

....

....

....

(Total for Question 3 is 3 marks)

4   (a) Work out 24×100

....
(1)

(b) Work out $7 + 4 + 9 + 4 + 2 + 8 + 1 + 3$

....
(1)

(c) Work out $3003 - 404$

....
(2)
(Total for Question 4 is 4 marks)

5   The table gives information about six mobile phones

Phone	Cost	Recharge time (minutes)	Weight (grams)	4G-compatible
C9090	£89.50	90	90	
D404	£175	210	121	✓
G103	£205	160	104	✓
G405	£39.95	85	83	
X12	£100	160	87	
X4A	£275	180	111	✓

(a) Which phone is the heaviest?

....
(1)

(b) Which phones cost less than £150?

....
(1)

(c) Which phone is 4G-compatible **and** has a recharge time of 160 minutes?

....
(1)
(Total for Question 5 is 3 marks)

6   Here is a list of numbers.

$$2 \quad 7 \quad 9 \quad 11 \quad 12 \quad 42 \quad 45$$

From the list,

(a)   write down an even number greater than 10

....
(1)

(b)   write down a square number

....
(1)

(c)   write down a multiple of 4

....
(1)

(d)   write down a factor of 6

....
(1)

(Total for Question 6 is 4 marks)

---

7   The diagram shows information about the height of a chair.
It also shows the height of the seat of the chair from the floor.

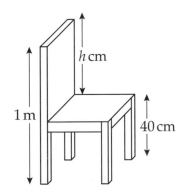

Diagram **NOT**
drawn accurately

What is the height, h, of the back of the chair?

.... cm

(Total for Question 7 is 2 marks)

8   The diagram shows a circle, centre O.

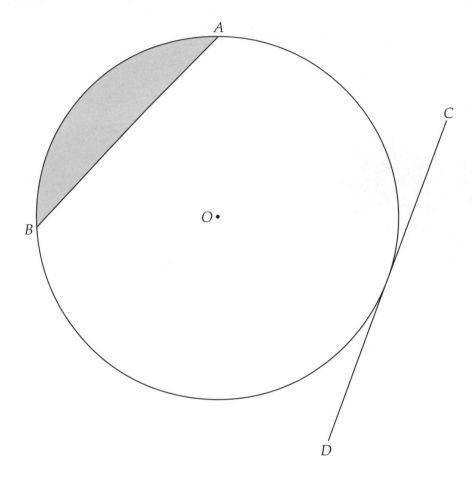

(a) Write down the length of the radius of the circle.

.... cm
(1)

(b) What is the mathematical name of the line CD?

....
(1)

(c) What is the mathematical name of the straight line AB?

....
(1)

(d) What is the mathematical name of the curved line AB?

....
(1)

(e) What is the mathematical name of the shaded area?

....
(1)
(Total for Question 8 is 5 marks)

9 Jasmine's pay is worked out using this rule.

$$\boxed{\text{Pay} = £8 \times \text{number of hours worked}}$$

On Monday Jasmine works for 4 hours.

(a) Work out her pay for Monday.

£ ....

(2)

On Tuesday Jasmine's pay is £52

(b) How many hours does she work on Tuesday?

.... hours

(2)

(Total for Question 9 is 4 marks)

10 Find the value of $3x + 5y$ when $x = 3$ and $y = 4$

....

(Total for Question 10 is 2 marks)

11 Aden buys

one pineapple costing £1.55
one mango costing 99p
two melons.

Aden pays with a £5 note.
He gets 20p change.

Work out the cost of **one** melon.

£..................................
(Total for Question 11 is 3 marks)

12 In a sale, full prices are reduced by $\frac{1}{3}$

The full price of a crash helmet is £180

What is the sale price of the crash helmet?

£..................................
(Total for Question 12 is 3 marks)

*13 Tammy makes and sells paperweights.
The paperweights are posted in boxes in the shape of a cuboid.

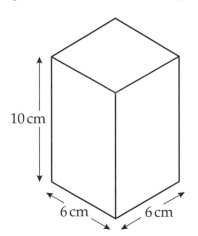

Diagram **NOT**
drawn accurately

10 cm

6 cm   6 cm

Tammy sketches five designs for the net of the box.

1

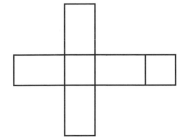

2

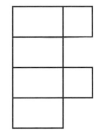

3

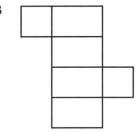

4

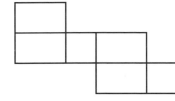

5

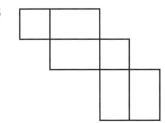

Tammy wants her design to fit on a 25 cm × 25 cm square card.

Which design should Tammy choose?
Give reasons for your answer.
Give reasons why she should not choose the other designs.

(Total for Question 13 is 4 marks)

14   This is a conversion graph for British pounds (£) and Australian dollars ($).

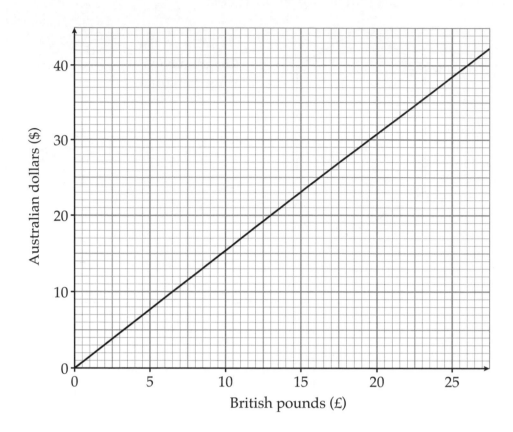

British pounds (£)

(a)   Use the conversion graph to change:
    (i) 10 British pounds (£) to Australian dollars ($)

$ ....
(1)

    (ii) 20 Australian dollars ($) to British pounds (£).

£ ....
(1)

(b)   Change 90 Australian dollars ($) into British pounds (£).

£ ....
(2)
(Total for Question 14 is 4 marks)

15   The bar chart shows the number of job applications Susan sent during one week.

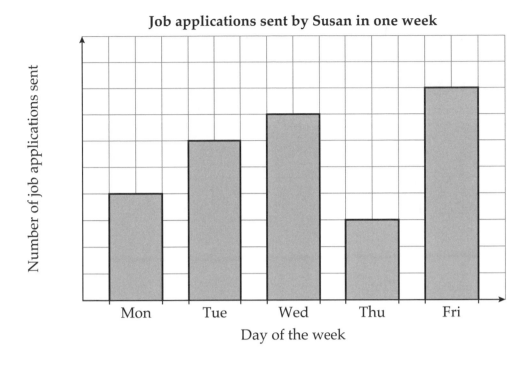

On Tuesday Susan sent 12 job applications.

How many job applications did Susan send altogether during this week?
You must show your working.

....

(Total for Question 15 is 5 marks)

16   Work out 342×12

....

(Total for Question 16 is 3 marks)

---

17   (a)   Write $\frac{3}{4}$ as a decimal.

....

(1)

(b)   Simplify $\frac{20}{24}$

Give your answer in its simplest form.

....

(1)

(c)   Daniel says $\frac{3}{5}$ is larger than $\frac{2}{3}$

Is he right?
Explain your answer.

....

....

....

(3)

(Total for Question 17 is 5 marks)

18 Here is part of a train timetable from Milford Haven to Manchester.

Milford Haven to Manchester

Milford Haven	06 00	07 05	09 08	11 08	13 08
Swansea	07 45	08 55	10 55	12 54	14 55
Cardiff	08 50	10 05	12 05	14 05	15 50
Hereford	09 51	11 06	13 06	15 06	16 53
Shrewsbury	10 53	11 58	13 58	15 58	17 50
Manchester	12 15	13 15	15 15	17 14	19 15

A train leaves Milford Haven at 06 00

(a) At what time should it arrive in Manchester?

....
(1)

Another train leaves Cardiff at 15 50

(b) Work out how many minutes this train should take to go from Cardiff to Hereford.

....
(1)

Lynn lives in Milford Haven.

She has a meeting in Shrewsbury at 14 00
When Lynn arrives in Shrewsbury it takes 20 minutes to travel to her meeting.

(c) What is the time of the latest train she can take from Milford Haven to be on time for her meeting?

....
(1)
(Total for Question 18 is 3 marks)

19   The Angel of the North is a statue.
     The statue is 20 m tall.

Penny makes a model of the statue.
She uses a scale of 1 : 25

What is the height of the model of the statue?
Give your answer in centimetres.

.... cm

(Total for Question 19 is 3 marks)

*20 Emir works 120 hours per month.
He is paid £8 per hour.

His rent is £400 per month.

Emir gets a pay rise of 5%.

His rent increases to £430 per month.

Is Emir better off or worse off each month?
You must show your working.

(Total for Question 20 is 5 marks)

*21 A fair three-sided spinner has sections labelled 1, 2 and 4
A fair four-sided dice has faces labelled 1, 2, 3 and 4

The spinner is spun and the dice is rolled at the same time.
The number the spinner lands on is added to the number shown on the dice to give
a total score.

Work out the probability that the total score is less than 5

....
(Total for Question 21 is 3 marks)

22 Femke asked 100 adults where they spent their summer holiday.
Each adult either spent their holiday in the UK or they spent their holiday abroad.

Of the 36 people who spent their holiday in the UK, 26 were men.
35 women asked spent their holiday abroad.

How many more men spent their holiday abroad than in the UK?

....
(Total for Question 22 is 4 marks)

23 (a)   Estimate $\sqrt{27}$

Explain how you got your answer.

....

....

(2)

(b)   Work out an estimate for $\dfrac{21.4 \times 6.88}{0.52}$

....

(3)

(Total for Question 23 is 5 marks)

*24

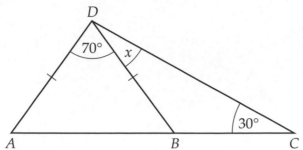

Diagram **NOT** drawn accurately

ABC is a straight line.
$BD = AD$.
Angle $BCD = 30°$.
Angle $ADB = 70°$.

Work out the size of the angle marked x.
Give reasons for your answer.

(Total for Question 24 is 4 marks)

25 Sam wanted to find out which holiday destinations are popular with families.
He interviewed people at Luton airport in January.

(a) His sample is biased.
Give two reasons to show his sample is biased.

1 ....

....

....

2 ....

....

....

(2)

(b) Write a suitable question Sam could use to find out which holiday destinations are popular with families.

(2)

(Total for Question 25 is 4 marks)

26 In a restaurant, tables can be placed together for large numbers of people.

The diagram shows chairs arranged around tables.

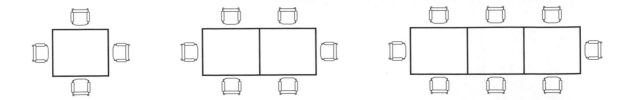

(a) How many chairs are needed for six tables placed together?

....

(2)

(b) Find an expression, in terms of n, for the number of chairs at n tables.

....

(2)

(Total for Question 26 is 4 marks)

27 (a) Simplify $y^6 \div y^3$

....
(1)

(b) Simplify $3x^3 \times 4x^5$

....
(2)
(Total for Question 27 is 3 marks)

TOTAL FOR PAPER IS 100 MARKS

1   (a) Write down the number 3456 in words.

....

(1)

(b) Write the number **eight thousand two hundred and six** in figures.

....

(1)

(c) Write down the value of the digit **5** in the number 3571

....

(1)

(Total for Question 1 is 3 marks)

2   Here are the names of seven rabbits.

Abbi   Pi   Emma   Patch   Gill   Penny   Polly

Sandra picks one rabbit at random.

Circle the correct word that describes the probability that Sandra picks a rabbit that:

(a) has a name that contains four letters

impossible   unlikely   evens   likely   certain

(1)

(b) has a name that begins with the letter P

impossible   unlikely   evens   likely   certain

(1)

(c) has a name that ends with the letter S.

impossible   unlikely   evens   likely   certain

(1)

(Total for Question 2 is 3 marks)

3 The shaded shape is drawn on a grid of centimetre squares.

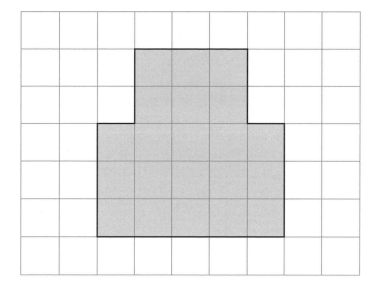

(a) (i) Work out the area of the shaded shape.

.... cm²
(1)

(ii) Work out the perimeter of the shaded shape.

.... cm
(1)

This is a solid prism made of centimetre cubes.

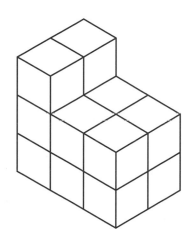

Diagram **NOT**
drawn accurately

(b) Work out the volume of the prism.

.... cm³
(1)
(Total for Question 3 is 3 marks)

4   Tyson has a £10 note to spend on lemonade.

     A bottle of lemonade costs 78p.

     He buys as many bottles of lemonade as possible.

     Work out how much change Tyson should get.

.... p

(Total for Question 4 is 3 marks)

5   The table shows the temperature, in °C, at midday on a winter's day in six towns.

Town	York	Selby	Wakefield	Worksop	Lincoln	Burwell
Temperature (°C)	1	−1	−4	0	−2	−3

(a) Which town
     (i) had the lowest temperature at midday?

....

(1)

     (ii) had the highest temperature at midday?

....

(1)

The midday temperature in Sheffield was 5°C higher than the midday temperature in Burwell.

(b) Work out the midday temperature in Sheffield.

...................................°C

(1)

(Total for Question 5 is 3 marks)

6 (a) What fraction of this shape is shaded?

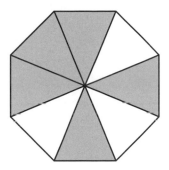

....
(1)

(b) Convert 0.7 to a fraction.

....
(1)

(c) What percentage of this shape is shaded?

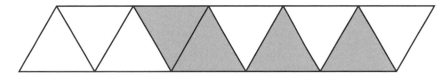

...................................%
(1)
(Total for Question 6 is 3 marks)

7   Sam made a list of his last 9 test marks.

9   4   5   8   5   5   8   9   10

(a) Write down the mode.

....
(1)

(b) Work out the range.

....
(2)

(c) Work out the mean.

....
(2)
(Total for Question 7 is 5 marks)

8 (a) Put these numbers in order, starting with the smallest.

$$4 \quad 6 \quad -2 \quad 0 \quad -7$$

....

(1)

(b) Put these numbers in order, starting with the smallest.

$$7.2 \quad 7.8 \quad 7.25 \quad 7.15$$

....

(1)

(Total for Question 8 is 2 marks)

9 (a) Simplify $8a - 3a$

....

(1)

(b) Simplify $3b \times 3b$

....

(1)

(c) Simplify $c^2 + c^2$

....

(1)

(d) Simplify $5d + 4e - 3d + e$

....

(2)

(Total for Question 9 is 5 marks)

10 (a) Measure the size of the angle marked x.

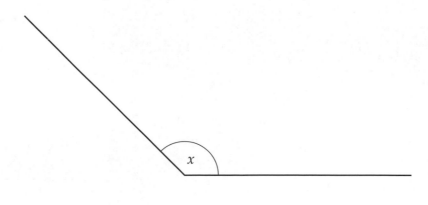

.... °

(1)

The diagram shows three angles.

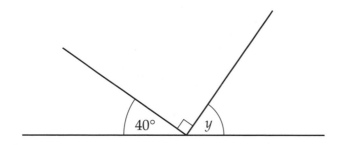

Diagram **NOT**
drawn accurately

(b) (i) Work out the value of y.

.... °

(2)

(ii) Give a reason for your answer.

....

....

(1)

(Total for Question 10 is 4 marks)

11 Dianne completes a weekly bar chart that shows the numbers of men and women who gave positive feedback to a supermarket questionnaire.

This is the bar chart for one week.

The bar for men on Friday is missing.

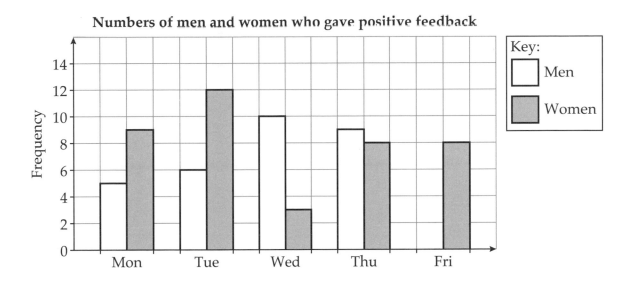

Numbers of men and women who gave positive feedback

Key:
☐ Men
▨ Women

(a) How many women gave positive feedback on Tuesday?

....

(1)

Dianne knows that over the whole week the total number of men who gave positive feedback was the same as the total number of women.

(b) How many men gave positive feedback on Friday?

....

(4)

(Total for Question 11 is 5 marks)

12 The table shows some information on how Tom spends his wages.

Item	Percentage of wages spent
Food	21%
Clothing	8%
Rent	41%
Entertainment	.........%
Other	15%

(a) Complete the table.

(2)

Last month Tom's wages were £1550

(b) How much of his wages did he spend on rent?

£.................................

(2)

(Total for Question 12 is 4 marks)

13

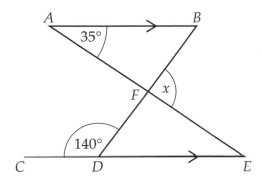

Diagram **NOT**
drawn accurately

The lines *AB* and *CE* are parallel.
Angle *BAF* is 35°.
Angle *CDF* is 140°.

Work out the size of angle *BFE*, labelled *x*.

.... °

(Total for Question 13 is 4 marks)

14

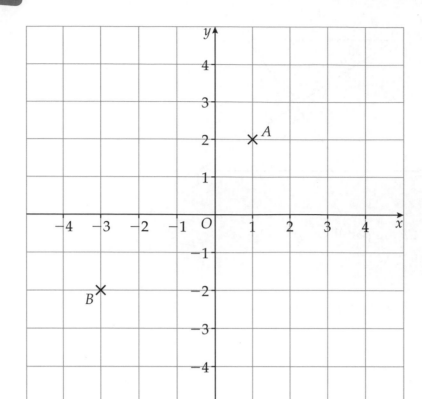

(a) Write down the coordinates of the point *A*.

(.................., ...)
(1)

(b) Write down the coordinates of the point *B*.

(.................., ...)
(1)

(c) On the grid, plot the point (−3, 3) with a cross (✗).
Label this point *C*.

(1)

(d) Write down the coordinates of the midpoint of *AB*.

(.................., ...)
(1)
(Total for Question 14 is 4 marks)

15 (a) Shade in **three** more squares on the diagram, to make a pattern with 1 line of symmetry.

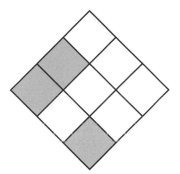

(2)

(b) Shade in **three** more squares on the diagram, to make a pattern with an order of rotational symmetry of 4

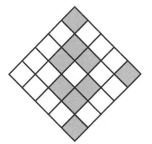

(1)

(c) This large square is made from squares of different sizes.

What fraction of the large square is shaded?

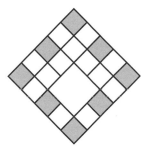

....

(2)

(Total for Question 15 is 5 marks)

16 A magazine uses a pictogram to show the average house price in five different
    English counties.
    The key for the pictogram is missing.

Lancashire	
Herefordshire	
Essex	
Surrey	
Lincolnshire	

Key:

The average house price in Herefordshire is £225 000

The average house price in Lincolnshire is £125 000

(a) Complete the pictogram to show this information.
     Include a key for the pictogram.

(3)

(b) Work out the average house price in Essex.

£.....................................

(2)

(Total for Question 16 is 5 marks)

*17 David is shopping in a supermarket.
All of the items he buys are on special offer.

The table shows what he buys.

Item	Price each	Special offer	Number he buys
Loaf of bread	£1.25	Buy 2 for £2	2
Bag of dog food	£4.90	3 for the price of 2	3
Pizza	£2.40	Buy 1, get the 2nd for half price	2

What is the total amount of money that David saves by using the special offers?
You must show your working.

£.................................

(Total for Question 17 is 5 marks)

18 (a) Solve $x + 7 = 18$

$x = $ ....
(1)

(b) Solve $5y = 30$

$y = $ ....
(1)

(c) Solve $\frac{x}{3} = 9$

$x = $ ....
(1)

(d) Solve $4y - 6 = 10$

$y = $ ....
(2)

(Total for Question 18 is 5 marks)

19 The diagram shows a square and an equilateral triangle.

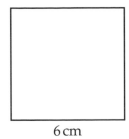 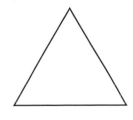

Diagram **NOT**
drawn accurately

6 cm

The perimeter of the square is the same as the perimeter of the equilateral triangle.

Work out the length of one side of the equilateral triangle.

.... cm

(Total for Question 19 is 4 marks)

20 Use your calculator to work out

(a) 13.4^2

....

(1)

(b) $16.5 - \sqrt{17.64}$

....

(2)

(Total for Question 20 is 3 marks)

*21 A supermarket sells strawberries in boxes of two different sizes.

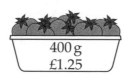

400 g
£1.25

900 g
£2.95

Which is the better value for money?
You must show your working.

(Total for Question 21 is 3 marks)

*22 Leslie has a holiday job in Spain.
She needs to drive from Murcia to Santander.

This chart gives the driving distances, in kilometres, between different cities in Spain.

Alicante				
429	Madrid			
82	407	Murcia		
875	452	840	Santander	
494	312	544	398	Zaragoza

Leslie knows that 5 miles is about the same as 8 km.
She will drive at an average speed of 50 mph.

How long will it take her to drive from Murcia to Santander?
You must show your working.
Give your answer in hours and minutes.

(Total for Question 22 is 5 marks)

23

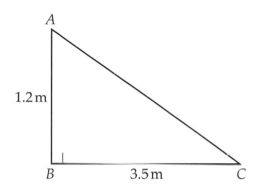

ABC is a right-angled triangle.
AB = 1.2 m.
BC = 3.5 m.

Calculate the length of *AC*.

.... m
(Total for Question 23 is 3 marks)

*24 The diagram shows a porch in the shape of a rectangle.

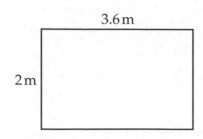

3.6 m

2 m

Diagram **NOT** drawn accurately

The porch is 3.6 m long and 2 m wide.

Dennis is going to cover the floor of the porch with square floor tiles.

Each floor tile is a square of side 40 cm.
Dennis buys 48 of the floor tiles.

Does Dennis buy enough floor tiles to cover the floor of the porch?
You must show all your working.

(Total for Question 24 is 3 marks)

25 A perfume house is making two new fragrances.
Each bottle contains 350 m*l*.

'Sparkle' contains cedarwood and lavender in the ratio 2 : 5
'Shimmer' contains cedarwood and lavender in the ratio 5 : 12

Which fragrance, Sparkle or Shimmer, has the greater amount of cedarwood?
You must show your working.

....

(Total for Question 25 is 3 marks)

*26 Miss Jebson makes an artwork for the wall of her school hall.

The artwork is made from a square panel of wood.
She cuts one rectangular hole and two circular holes out of the square panel of wood.

Each circle has a diameter of 30 cm.
The rectangle is 90 cm long and 20 cm wide.

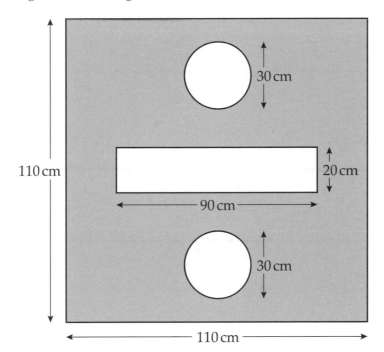

Diagram **NOT**
drawn accurately

Miss Jebson is going to paint the front of the artwork with one coat of paint.
One pot of paint covers 2500 cm².

How many pots of paint does Miss Jebson need?
You must show your working.

(Total for Question 26 is 5 marks)

TOTAL FOR PAPER IS 100 MARKS

1   (a)

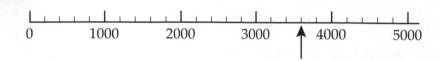

Write down the number marked by the arrow.

....

(1)

(b)

Find the number −18 on the number scale.

Mark the number with an arrow ⬆.

(1)

(c)

Write down the number marked by the arrow.

....

(1)

(Total for Question 1 is 3 marks)

2 The clocks show the time in London and in San Francisco.

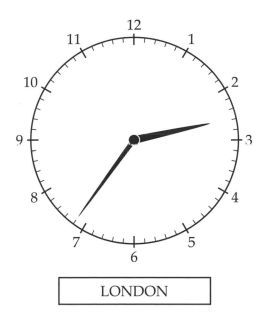

| LONDON | | SAN FRANCISCO |

It is afternoon in London.

(a) Write down the time in London using the 24-hour clock.

....

(1)

It is morning in San Francisco when it is afternoon in London.

The time in London is ahead of the time in San Francisco.

(b) How many hours is London ahead of San Francisco?

.... hours

(1)

(Total for Question 2 is 2 marks)

3   The diagram shows a square-based pyramid.

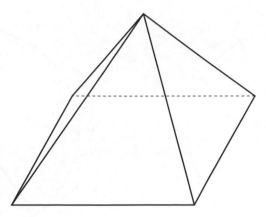

(a) How many faces does the shape have?

....
(1)

(b) How many vertices does the shape have?

....
(1)

(c) How many edges does the shape have?

....
(1)

(Total for Question 3 is 3 marks)

4

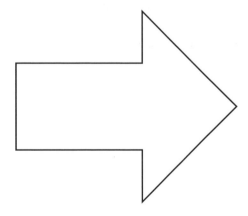

(a) Mark, with the letter *P*, a right angle.

(1)

(b) Mark, with the letter *R*, a reflex angle.

(1)

(c) Mark with arrows (>) two lines that are parallel.

(1)

(Total for Question 4 is 3 marks)

5   (a)   Write down all of the common factors of 24 and 40

....

(2)

(b)   Write down all of the prime numbers between 25 and 35

....

(2)

(Total for Question 5 is 4 marks)

6   On 27 February, Liam checks his bank statement for February so far.

Date	Details	Paid Out (£)	Paid In (£)	Balance (£)
				648.00
08/02/2013	South Electric	108.50		
18/02/2013	Trent Builders	745.00		
18/02/2013	MDM Insurance	13.50		
25/02/2013	Cheque 08829932		123.00	
26/02/2013	Top Nosh	53.00		

Liam started the month with £648.00 in his bank account.

How much does he need to pay in if he is to finish the month with £100 in his bank account?
Show all of your working.

£.................................

(Total for Question 6 is 5 marks)

7

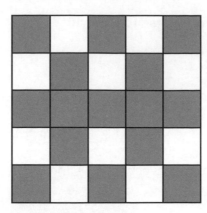

(a)   What fraction of the shape is shaded?
      Give your answer as a fraction in its simplest form.

....
(2)

(b)   (i)   Write 17% as a fraction.

....
(1)

      (ii) Write your answer to (i) as a decimal.

....
(1)
(Total for Question 7 is 4 marks)

8 Greta cut this shape from a 6 cm wide roll of cloth.
   The shape is drawn on a centimetre grid.

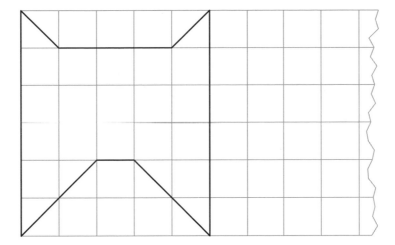

(a) Work out the area of the shape.

.... cm²
(2)

The roll of cloth is 4 metres long.

(b) How many shapes could Greta cut from the roll?

....
(3)
(Total for Question 8 is 5 marks)

9 1 kg is about 2.2 pounds.

(a) Give an estimate for 15 kg in pounds.

.... pounds
(2)

1 gallon is about 4.5 litres.

(b) Give an estimate for 36 litres in gallons.

.... gallons
(2)
(Total for Question 9 is 4 marks)

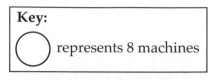

10 Nino carried out a survey about the exercise machines in some houses in his street.

He found there were 56 exercise machines altogether.

He started to draw this pictogram to show his results.

Rowing machine	◯ ◿
Exercise bike	
Stepper	
Treadmill	

Key:

◯ represents 8 machines

(a) How many rowing machines were there?

....
(1)

There were 16 exercise bikes.

(b) Show this information on the pictogram.

(1)

Nino found that there were twice as many steppers as treadmills.

(c) Complete the pictogram.

(2)
(Total for Question 10 is 4 marks)

11 Here are some patterns made from the letter B.

B   **B B**   **B B B**

B B   **B B B**   **B B B B**

Pattern 1   Pattern 2   Pattern 3

(a) Draw Pattern 4

(1)

(b) Work out the number of times the letter B is used in Pattern 10

....

(2)

(Total for Question 11 is 3 marks)

12 (a) Fill in 5 squares of the grid below.
    Your shape must have exactly 4 lines of symmetry.

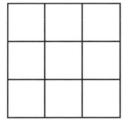

(1)

(b) Fill in 5 squares of the grid below.
    Your shape must have rotational symmetry of order 2

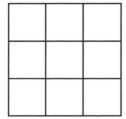

(1)

(Total for Question 12 is 2 marks)

13 (a) Work out $7 - 4 \times 5 - 3$

....
(2)

(b) Write $4 \times 4 \times 4 \times 4 \times 4$ using index notation.

....
(1)

(c) Work out the value of $10^3 \div 5^2$

....
(2)

(d) A candle burns down 0.8 cm every hour.

How long will it take to burn down 16 cm?

.... hours
(2)
(Total for Question 13 is 7 marks)

14 (a) Simplify $9m - m$

....
(1)

(b) Simplify $5k - 2p - 3k + 6p$

....
(2)

(c) Solve $h - 11 = 12$

$h =$ ....
(1)

(d) Solve $3x - 4 = 17$

$x =$ ....
(2)
(Total for Question 14 is 6 marks)

15 These letters are placed in a bag.

A letter is taken at random from the bag.

(a) Write down the probability that the letter is E.

....
(2)

(b) On the probability scale, mark with a cross (✗) the probability that the letter is A.

|_____|_____|
0   1

(1)

(c) Write down the probability that the letter is **not** E.

....
(1)
(Total for Question 15 is 4 marks)

16   The diagram shows the numbers of goals scored by a hockey team over a season.

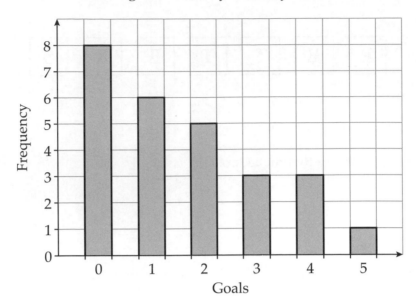

Fariq says that the team scored 3 or more goals just as often as they scored no goals.

Is he correct?
Give reasons for your answer.

....

....

(Total for Question 16 is 3 marks)

*17

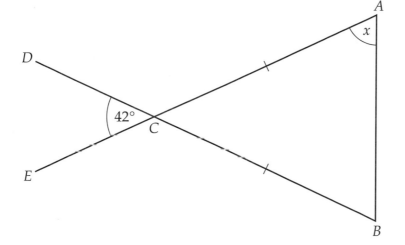

Diagram **NOT**
drawn accurately

BCD and *ACE* are straight lines.
AC = *BC*.

Work out the size of angle *x*.
Give reasons for your answer.

(Total for Question 17 is 4 marks)

18 The diagram shows a cuboid.

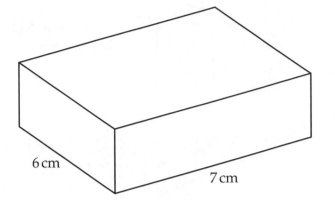

6 cm

7 cm

Diagram **NOT**
drawn accurately

The volume of the cuboid is 168 cm³.

Work out the height of the cuboid.

.... cm

(Total for Question 18 is 2 marks)

19 Mr Sharp runs a cookery shop.

He wants to find out how often his customers eat meat.

He decides to give a questionnaire to 25 customers who spent £25 to £30 in his shop.

(a) Give one reason why his sample may be biased.

(1)

(b) Write a suitable question for Mr Sharp's questionnaire.

(2)

(Total for Question 19 is 3 marks)

*20 These two card shops have special offers for Happy New Year cards.

Greetings
Happy New Year cards
£1.66 each
3 for the price of 2

For All Occasions
Happy New Year cards
£1.35 each
Every 4th card free

Melissa wants to buy 6 Happy New Year cards.

Melissa wants to buy the cards as cheaply as possible.
At which shop should she buy the cards?
Show all of your working.

(Total for Question 20 is 4 marks)

21 Four children each collected money for charity.
    The pie chart below shows how much each of them collected.

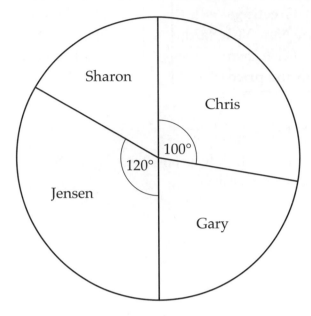

Gary and Sharon collected the same amount.
Jensen collected £60

Work out how much Sharon collected.
Show all of your working.

£ ....
(Total for Question 21 is 4 marks)

22 Terri mixed 300 g of rice with 240 g of fish.

She added some onion to the mixture.

The ratio of the weight of fish to the weight of onion was 3 : 2

Work out the ratio of the weight of rice to the weight of onion.

....

(Total for Question 22 is 3 marks)

23 The diagram shows a heptagon.

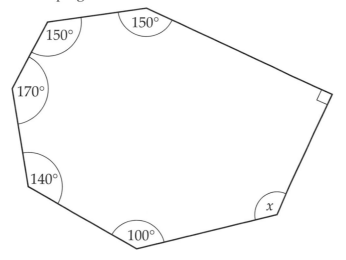

Diagram **NOT**
drawn accurately

Work out the size of angle x.

°

....

(Total for Question 23 is 3 marks)

101

24 On the grid, draw the graph of $y = 2x + 3$ for values of x from -3 to 2

(Total for Question 24 is 3 marks)

*25 These two rectangles have the same perimeter.

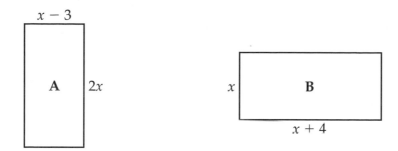

In the diagram, all of the measurements are in metres.

Work out the width and height of rectangle **A**.
Show all of your working.

(Total for Question 25 is 5 marks)

26 The scatter graph shows information about the number of people living in blocks of flats.
It shows the number of flats in a block and the total number of people living in the block.

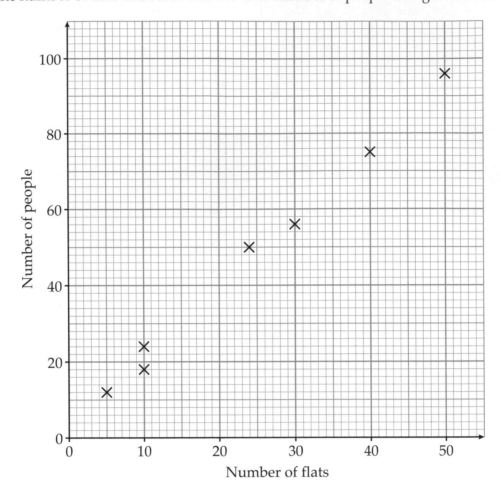

(a) What type of correlation does the scatter graph show?

....

(1)

38 people live in another block of 20 flats.

(b) Plot this information on the graph.

(1)

(c) Estimate the number of people living in a block of 36 flats.

....

(2)

(Total for Question 26 is 4 marks)

27 Three girls shared a full bottle of cola.

Karen drank $\frac{1}{4}$ of the bottle.

Rita drank $\frac{3}{10}$ of the bottle.

Megan drank the rest.

Work out the fraction of the bottle of cola which Megan drank.

....

(Total for Question 27 is 3 marks)

TOTAL FOR PAPER IS 100 MARKS

1   (a)   Write the number 30 205 in words.

    ....

                                                                                                    (1)

    (b)   Write down the value of the digit **3** in the number 2.3608

                                                                        ....

                                                                                                    (1)

    (c)   Write down the number 3 020 536 to the nearest thousand.

                                                                        ....

                                                                                                    (1)
                                                                        (Total for Question 1 is 3 marks)

2

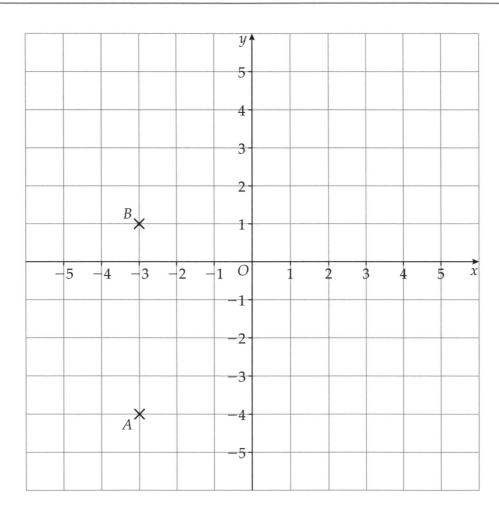

    (a)   Write down the coordinates of the point *A*.

                                                                        (................ , ...)
                                                                                                    (1)

    (b)   Plot the point *C* (3, 2) on the grid.

                                                                                                    (1)

    ABCD is a parallelogram.

    (c)   Mark the point *D* on the grid.

                                                                                                    (1)
                                                                        (Total for Question 2 is 3 marks)

3 Here is a quadrilateral.

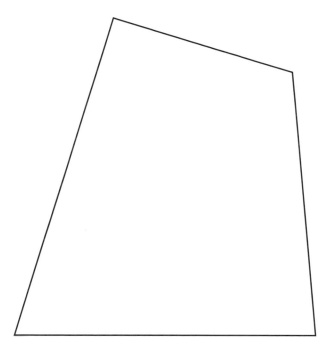

By measuring accurately, find the perimeter of the quadrilateral.

.... cm

(Total for Question 3 is 3 marks)

4 In a game, 5 players each put 12 counters on a table.

Sasha wins 35% of the counters.
Peter wins $\frac{2}{5}$ of the counters.
Haydon wins the remaining counters.

How many counters did Haydon win?
Show all of your working.

....

(Total for Question 4 is 4 marks)

5

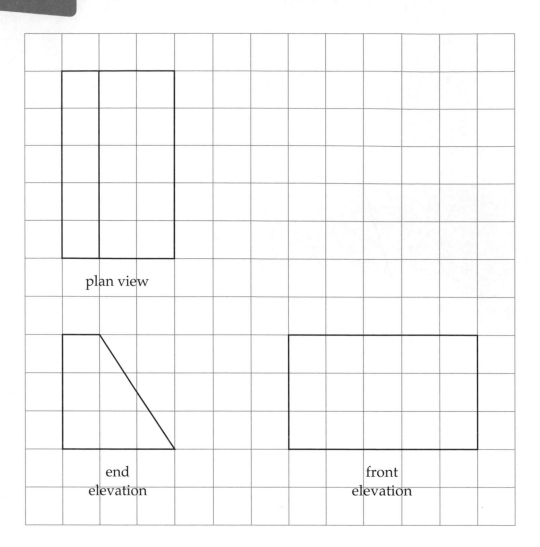

plan view

end
elevation

front
elevation

The diagram shows the plan view, end elevation and front elevation of a prism.
The diagram is drawn on a grid of centimetre squares.

Sketch the prism.
Show the dimensions on your diagram.

(Total for Question 5 is 3 marks)

6

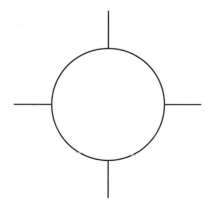

(a) How many lines of symmetry does the shape have?

....
(1)

(b) What is the order of rotational symmetry of the shaded shape below?

....
(1)

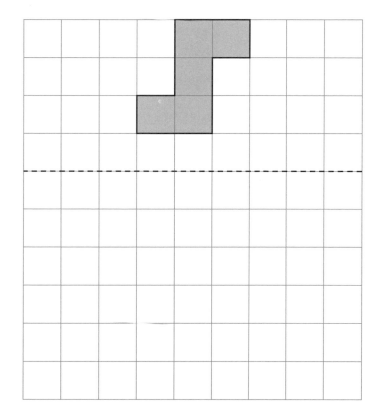

(c) Reflect the shaded shape in the dotted line.

(2)
(Total for Question 6 is 4 marks)

7   Table A show the distances, in miles, between some towns.

Table A

Birmingham	100	52	109	111	64
	Cambridge	118	145	54	80
		Gloucester	160	104	50
			Leeds	190	160
				London	56
					Oxford

Table B shows the cost of delivering a parcel the same day by a courier service.

Table B

		Distance (miles) up to			
		50	**100**	**150**	**200**
	5 kg	£42	£56	£64	£91
Weight	**10 kg**	£51	£72	£83	£126
up to	**20 kg**	£58	£87	£99	£152
	50 kg	£90	£121	£144	£215

Ramon has businesses in Birmingham, Gloucester and Leeds.

Work out the total cost for Ramon to send the following parcels.

  2 kg parcel from Birmingham to Gloucester

 43 kg from Gloucester to Leeds

 12 kg parcel from Leeds to Birmingham

£ ....

(Total for Question 7 is 4 marks)

*8   These conversion graphs can be used to convert between Pounds (£), Dollars ($) and Euros (€).

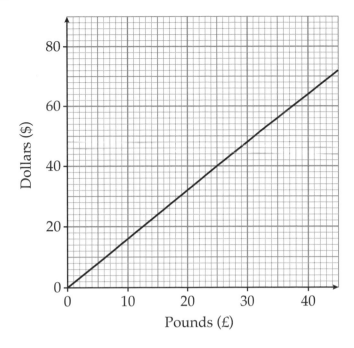

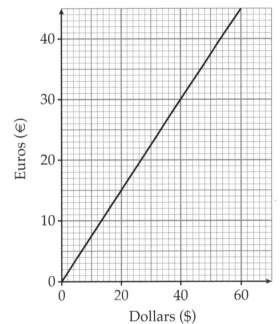

Warren has $20 and £20

Can he afford a radio that costs €45?

(Total for Question 8 is 3 marks)

*9   In a café, some people ordered the following types of coffee.

	Americano	Latte	Cappuccino	Espresso
Men	12	18	30	20
Women	6	28	36	16

Draw a suitable diagram to show the information in the table.
Use the grid below.

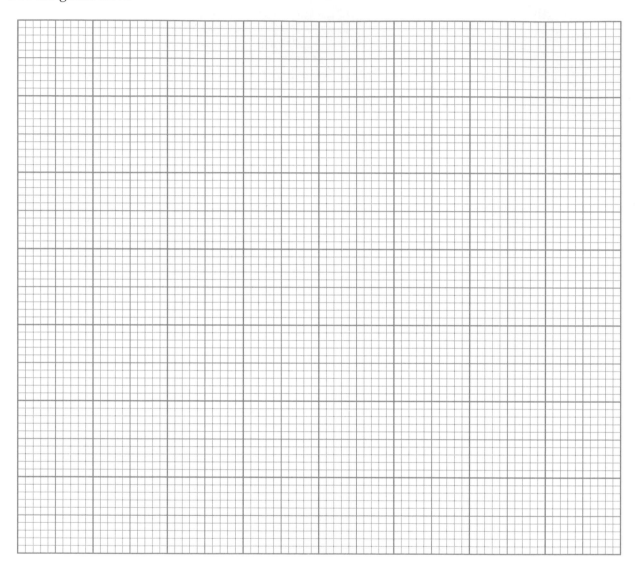

(Total for Question 9 is 4 marks)

10 Paula has saved £17.88 using 2p, 5p and 10p coins.

There are 464 coins altogether.

$\frac{1}{4}$ of the coins are 5p coins.

£6.40 is in 10p coins.
The rest of the coins are 2p coins

Work out the number of 2p coins.
Show all your working.

....
(Total for Question 10 is 4 marks)

11 Clarissa wants to put two coats of paint on the walls of her lounge.

The walls have a total area of 47 m².

A 2 litre tin of paint costs £6.99
2 litres of paint cover an area of 24 m².

How much will it cost for Clarissa to paint the walls of her lounge?

£ ....
(Total for Question 11 is 4 marks)

12 Here are the instructions for cooking a piece of meat.

25 minutes per 500 g plus 30 minutes extra

The meat weighs 2.5 kg.

Work out the time needed to cook the meat.

.... minutes
(Total for Question 12 is 4 marks)

13 Here is a list of numbers.

       51   48   2   53   50   48   1   52   55   49

(a) Work out the median.

....

(2)

(b) Work out the mean.

....

(2)

(c) Work out the range.

....

(1)

(Total for Question 13 is 5 marks)

14

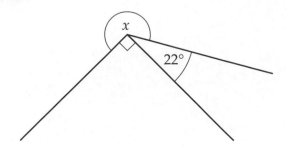

Diagram **NOT**
drawn accurately

(a)   Why is it impossible for angle x to be 238°?

....

....

(1)

(b)

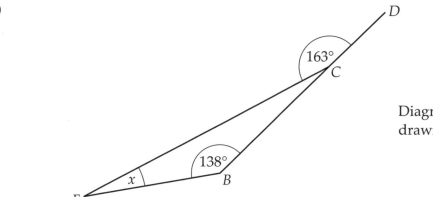

Diagram **NOT**
drawn accurately

BCD is a straight line.
BEC is a triangle.
Angle *DCE* = 163°.
Angle *EBD* = 138°.

Work out the size of the angle x.

.... °

(3)

(Total for Question 14 is 4 marks)

15 (a) (i) Write down $\sqrt{60}$
Show all the figures on your calculator display.

....

(1)

(ii) Give your answer to (i) correct to 2 decimal places.

....

(1)

(b) Calculate the exact value of $2.6^3 - 1.2^4$

....

(2)

(Total for Question 15 is 4 marks)

16 Write these numbers in order of size, from smallest to largest.

$$0.63 \qquad 58\% \qquad \frac{3}{5}$$

....

(Total for Question 16 is 2 marks)

17

$3a + 1$

Diagram **NOT**
drawn accurately

$2b$

In the diagram, all measurements are in centimetres.

(a) Write a formula for the perimeter, P cm, of this rectangle.

....

(3)

(b) Work out the perimeter of the rectangle when $a = 5.5$ and $b = 0.4$

.... cm

(2)

(Total for Question 17 is 5 marks)

---

18 The three faces of a spinner are numbered 1, 2 and 3

The table shows the results of spinning the spinner 120 times.

Number	Frequency
1	61
2	22
3	37

Do you think the spinner is biased?
Explain your answer.

....

....

(Total for Question 18 is 1 mark)

19 Leandro asked 45 people if they are on Twitter or Facebook or neither.
The table shows his results.

Neither	Twitter	Facebook
10	25	30

Work out the number of people who are on both Twitter and Facebook.

....

(Total for Question 19 is 2 marks)

20 An aeroplane travels 805 miles at a speed of 575 mph.

How long does the journey take?
Give your answer in minutes.

.... minutes

(Total for Question 20 is 3 marks)

21 The diagram shows two types of plastic building block.

A
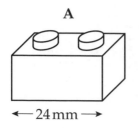
←— 24 mm —→

B
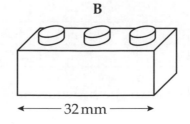
←——— 32 mm ———→

Diagram **NOT**
drawn accurately

Block A is 24 mm long.
Block B is 32 mm long.

Jeremy joins some type A blocks together make a straight row.
He then joins some type B blocks together to make a straight row of the same length.

Write down the shortest possible length of this row.

.... mm
(Total for Question 21 is 2 marks)

22 Alec asked a group of people how many text messages they sent yesterday.
The table shows the results.

Number	Frequency
0–4	38
5–9	24
10–14	22
15–19	15
20–24	15

Work out an estimate for the mean of the data.

....
(Total for Question 22 is 4 marks)

23 The equation

$$\frac{x^2}{1 + x} = 2$$

has a solution between 2 and 3

Use a trial improvement method to find this solution.
Give your answer correct to 1 decimal place.
You must show all your working.

$x = $ ....
(Total for Question 23 is 4 marks)

24 (a) Factorise $12m - 16n$

....
(1)

(b) Factorise completely $10m^2 - 5m$

....
(2)
(Total for Question 24 is 3 marks)

25   The diagram shows the position of a surveyor, S, and Disneyland, D.

×D

N

S

The surveyor can see the Eiffel Tower 32 km away on a bearing of 021°.

(a)   Using a scale of 1 cm to 4 km, mark the position of the Eiffel Tower with the letter E.

(2)

(b)   How far is the surveyor from Disneyland?

.... km

(2)

(Total for Question 25 is 4 marks)

26   Taahir weighs each potato in a bag.
     These are his results.

200 g	221 g	184 g	199 g	223 g
190 g	190 g	186 g	206 g	219 g
186 g	205 g	206 g	192 g	198 g

(a)   Complete the stem and leaf diagram for the data.

Key:

(3)

Taahir finds another potato in the bag that weighs 220 g.

(b)   Has the range of weights changed?
      Give a reason for your answer.

....

....

(1)

(Total for Question 26 is 4 marks)

27 Liz stood next to her dog Jock.

She threw a stick 40 metres away from them.

Jock took 8 seconds to reach the stick, running at a constant speed.

He spent 2 seconds picking up the stick.

Jock ran back to Liz at a constant speed of 4 m/s.

Use the grid below to draw a distance–time graph.

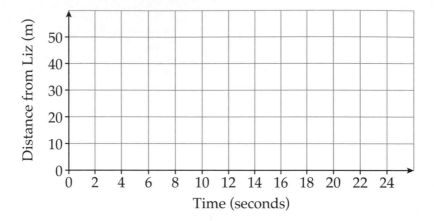

(Total for Question 27 is 3 marks)

28

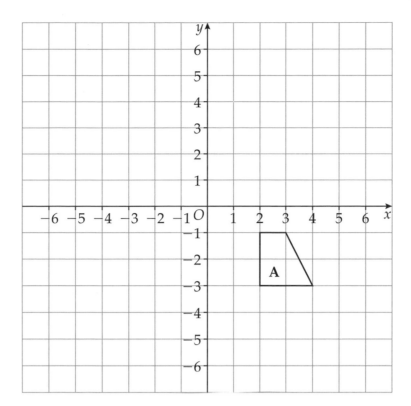

(a) Rotate shape **A** 90° anti-clockwise about the origin (0, 0).
   Label the image **B**.

(2)

(b) Reflect the shape **B** in the line with equation $x = 0$
   Label the image **C**.

(2)
(Total for Question 28 is 4 marks)

29

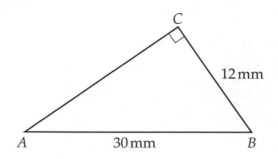

Diagram **NOT**
drawn accurately

The diagram shows a right-angled triangle *ABC*.

Work out the length of *AC*.
Give your answer correct to 1 decimal place.

.... mm
(Total for Question 29 is 3 marks)

TOTAL FOR PAPER IS 100 MARKS

1 (a)

Write down the number marked by the arrow.

> There are 5 subdivisions between each whole number, so each one is worth 0.2.

2.4 ✓

(1)

(b)

Find the number 370 on the number line above.

Mark the number with an arrow (↑).

> There are 10 subdivisions between each hundred, so each one is worth 10.

(1)

(c)

Write down the number marked by the arrow.

> There are 3 subdivisions between 40 and 46, so each one is worth 2. Count on in 2s until you get to the arrow.

60 ✓✓

(2)

(Total for Question 1 is 4 marks)

---

2 Garcia and Nakti visited a fish shop and got this bill.

FRESH FRY

Cod & 2 portions of chips	£5.75
4 sausages	£5.16
Cod & chips	£4.80

Garcia paid using a £20 note.

(a) How much change did he receive?

```
   5.75
   5.16
+  4.80
  15.71  ✓
```

20 − 15.71 = 4.29 ✓

> You can use a mental method to work out 20 − 15.71. Count on in steps from 15.71 to 20.
>
> +0.29 ... +4
>
> 15.71 16 20
>
> In total you have counted on 0.29 + 4 = 4.29.

£ 4.29 ✓

(3)

(b) What is the cost of one sausage?

```
   1.29
4)5.1³6  ✓
```

> 4 sausages cost £5.16, so divide 5.16 by 4 to work out the cost of one sausage.

£ 1.29 ✓

(2)

(Total for Question 2 is 5 marks)

---

3 Here are the first five terms of a sequence.

7, 12, 17, 22, 27
   +5 +5 +5 +5

> Write down the difference between each pair of terms to look for a pattern. The term-to-term rule for this sequence is +5.

(a) Write down the next term in the sequence.

27 + 5 = 32

32 ✓

(1)

Here are some terms of another sequence.

32, 16, 8, ⋯, 2
   ÷2 ÷2 ÷2 ÷2

(b) Write down the missing term in this sequence.

> The term-to-term rule for this sequence is ÷ 2.
> Check that the rule works for all the terms in the sequence.

4 ✓

(1)

(Total for Question 3 is 2 marks)

---

*4 The table shows the types of television set in the houses of a street.

Year	Analogue TV	Digital TV
2002	20	0
2004	18	1
2006	18	7
2008	15	15
2010	9	16

Draw a suitable diagram to show the information in the table.

Use the grid below.

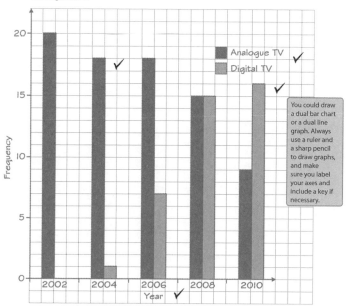

> You could draw a dual bar chart or a dual line graph. Always use a ruler and a sharp pencil to draw graphs, and make sure you label your axes and include a key if necessary.

(Total for Question 4 is 4 marks)

5 Here are two rectangles.

Rectangle **A** is drawn on a grid of centimetre squares.

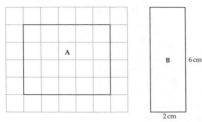

(a) Find the area of rectangle **A**.

$4 \times 5 = 20$

> Area of a rectangle = length × width

20 ✓ .... cm²
(1)

*(b) Which of the two rectangles has the greater perimeter?

Rectangle A
$5 + 5 + 4 + 4 = 18\,cm$ ✓

Rectangle B
$2 + 2 + 6 + 6 = 16\,cm$ ✓

Rectangle A has the greater perimeter. ✓

> This question has a star next to it, which means you can get marks for quality of written communication. You should show your working for both rectangles, and use the correct units (cm). Make sure you write down which rectangle has the greater perimeter.

(3)
(Total for Question 5 is 4 marks)

6 The pictogram shows the money collected by Year 10 for three different charities.

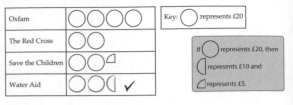

(a) Write down the amount collected for Oxfam.

$4 \times 20 = 80$

£ ....80........ ✓
(1)

(b) How much more money was collected for Save the Children than for the Red Cross?

$45 - 40 = 5$

> £20 + £20 + £5
> In total £45 was collected for Save the Children.

£ ....5........ ✓
(1)

£50 was collected for Water Aid.

(c) Use this information to complete the pictogram.

$50 = 20 + 20 + 10$

(1)
(Total for Question 6 is 3 marks)

7 The diagram shows an arrow that can rotate around the points of a compass.

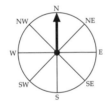

The angle rotates clockwise from N to E.

(a) (i) Write down the angle the arrow turns.

> There are 360° in a full turn, so there are 90° in a quarter turn.

90 ✓ °
(1)

(ii) Write down the special name for this angle.

Right angle ✓
(1)

The arrow rotates clockwise from W to E in three equal steps.

(b) Work out the angle the arrow turns in each step.

$180 \div 3 = 60$ ✓

> The arrow turns through 180° in three equal steps. Divide 180 by 3 to work out the size of each step.

60 ✓ °
(2)
(Total for Question 7 is 4 marks)

8 (a) Write down 80% as a fraction in its simplest form.

$\dfrac{80}{100} = \dfrac{8}{10} = \dfrac{4}{5}$ ✓

> Write a percentage as a fraction with denominator 100, then simplify your fraction.

$\dfrac{4}{5}$ ✓
(2)

(b) Which is the larger, $\dfrac{5}{6}$ or 75%?

You must show all your working.

$75\% = \dfrac{3}{4}$

$\dfrac{3}{4} = \dfrac{9}{12}$

$\dfrac{5}{6} = \dfrac{10}{12}$ ✓

> Write 75% as a fraction. To compare fractions, write them as equivalent fractions with the same denominator.

$\dfrac{5}{6}$ ✓
(2)
(Total for Question 8 is 4 marks)

9 Simon had c coins in his coin box.
He put 5 more coins into the coin box.

(a) Write down an expression, in terms of c, for the number of coins now in the box.

> Write '5 more than c' using algebra.

$c + 5$ ✓
(1)

Tara bought e eggs.
She used n eggs to make an omelette.

(b) Write down an expression, in terms of e and n, for the number of eggs Tara has left.

> Write 'n less than e' using algebra.

$e - n$ ✓
(1)
(Total for Question 9 is 2 marks)

10

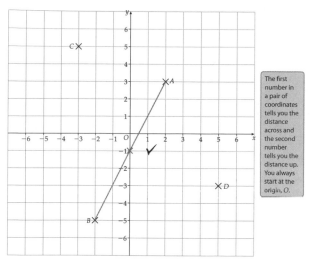

The first number in a pair of coordinates tells you the distance across and the second number tells you the distance up. You always start at the origin, O.

(a) Write down the letter of the point with coordinates (−3, 5).

3 squares to the left and 5 squares up.

C ✔

(1)

(b) Write down the coordinates of the point A.

2 squares to the right and 3 squares up.

(2 , 3) ✔

(1)

(c) Join the points A and B with a straight line.
Mark the midpoint of your line with a cross (✗).

(1)

Count squares to find the midpoint. From B you go 2 squares to the right and 4 squares up to get to the midpoint, then 2 squares to the right and 4 squares up again to get to A.

(Total for Question 10 is 3 marks)

11 Here are the winning numbers in a lottery game.

(6) (9) (21) (27) (31) (39)

(a) Which number is a prime number?

A prime number is only divisible by 1 and itself.

31 ✔

(1)

(b) Which number is a multiple of one of the other numbers?

27 = 3 × 9

27 ✔

(1)

(c) Which number is a square number?

9 = 3²

9 ✔

(1)

(Total for Question 11 is 3 marks)

12 (a) Write down the value of $\sqrt{64}$

8 ✔

(1)

(b) Work out 5 × (2 + 7)

Remember BIDMAS – Brackets, Indices, Division, Multiplication, Addition, Subtraction.

5 × 9 = 45

45 ✔

(1)

(Total for Question 12 is 2 marks)

13 (a) Draw all the lines of symmetry on this shape.

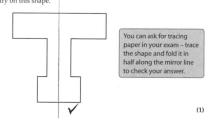

You can ask for tracing paper in your exam – trace the shape and fold it in half along the mirror line to check your answer.

✔

(1)

(b) Add **one** line to this shape to give it rotational symmetry of order 2

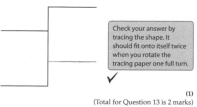

Check your answer by tracing the shape. It should fit onto itself twice when you rotate the tracing paper one full turn.

✔

(1)

(Total for Question 13 is 2 marks)

14 Here is part of a train timetable from Filton to Freshford.

Filton to Freshford

Filton	10 26	11 23	12 26	14 26	15 23
Bristol	10 49	11 49	12 39	14 48	15 44
Oldfield Park	11 03	11 56	12 53	15 02	15 58
Bath	11 07	12 07	12 57	15 06	16 02
Freshford	11 16	12 16	13 06	15 15	16 11

A train goes from Filton to Bath.
This train leaves Filton at 10 26

(a) Work out how many minutes the train takes to go from Filton to Bath.

34 + 7 = 41

Count on from 10 26 to 11 07 in two steps:
+34 mins   +7 mins
10 26 ⟶ 11 00 ⟶ 11 07

41 ✔

(1)

Marcus arrives at Filton station at 10 30

(b) What is the earliest time Marcus can now arrive in Bristol?

Marcus will have to catch the 11 23 from Filton.

11 49 ✔

(1)

Fiona arrives at Bristol station at 12 39

She visits a shopping mall in Bristol.
It takes 10 minutes to walk between the station and the shopping mall.
She wants to spend as long as possible in the shopping mall.

Fiona has arranged to meet a friend at Freshford station at 4.11 pm.

4.11 pm is 16 11 in the 24-hour clock.

(c) How long can Fiona spend in the shopping mall?

12 39 + 10 mins = 12 49
15 44 − 10 mins = 15 34 ✔

Work out what time Fiona gets to the shopping mall. Then work out what time she has to leave to catch the train which gets into Freshford at 16 11.

11 mins + 2 hours + 34 mins = 2 hours and 45 mins

2 hours 45 minutes ✔

(2)

(Total for Question 14 is 4 marks)

13

15 The stem and leaf diagram shows information about the number of houses in each road of a village.

0	8 8
1	4 4 7 9
2	0 0 6 8 8 8 9
3	0 2 2 5 5
4	6

Key:
3 | 2 represents 32 houses

(a) How many roads are there in the village?

> The total number of 'leaves' is the total number of data values.

19 ✔
(1)

(b) Work out the median number of houses.

> The median is the (19 + 1) ÷ 2 = 10th data value. Make sure you write down the actual data value and not just the 'leaf'.

28 ✔
(1)

(c) Work out the range.

46 − 8 = 38 ✔

> Range = largest value − smallest value

38 ✔
(2)
(Total for Question 15 is 4 marks)

16 (a) Simplify $e + e + e + e + e + e + e$

> There are 7 lots of e.
> 7e means $7 \times e$.

7e ✔
(1)

(b) Simplify $2p + 3q + 4p + q$

> Collect like terms. Remember that q means $1q$.

$2p + 4p + 3q + q = 6p + 4q$ ✔

$6p + 4q$ ✔
(2)

(c) Expand $3(m + 2n)$

> Multiply both terms inside the brackets by 3.
> $3(m + 2n) = 3 \times m + 3 \times 2n = 3m + 6n$

$3m + 6n$ ✔
(1)
(Total for Question 16 is 4 marks)

17 (a) Solve $t + 8 = 3$

> Subtract 8 from both sides of the equation.

$t = 3 - 8$

$t = -5$ ✔
(1)

(b) Solve $3w = 24$

> Divide both sides of the equation by 3.

$w = \dfrac{24}{3}$

$w = 8$ ✔
(1)

(c) Solve $4h + 5 = 13$

$4h = 13 - 5$ ✔
$4h = 8$
$h = \dfrac{8}{4}$

> You need to do two steps to get h on its own:
> • subtract 5 from both sides of the equation
> • divide both sides of the equation by 4.

$h = 2$ ✔
(2)
(Total for Question 17 is 4 marks)

18 Josh asked the students in his class about the sports they liked most.
The pie chart below shows the results.

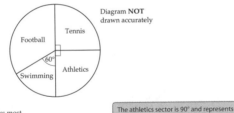

Diagram **NOT** drawn accurately

6 students liked athletics most.

How many liked football most?

> The athletics sector is 90° and represents 6 students, so divide 90 by 6 to work out the angle that represents one student. Subtract 60° from 180° to work out the size of the football sector, then divide this by 15 to work out how many students it represents.

Each student = 90° ÷ 6 = 15° ✔
Football sector = 180° − 60° = 120° ✔
120° ÷ 15° = 8

8 ✔
(Total for Question 18 is 3 marks)

19 (a) Write down 1 000 000 as a power of 10

> 10^n is 1 followed by n zeros.

10^6 ✔
(1)

(b) Work out $4^2 + 3^3$

> Remember BIDMAS – work out the indices (squares and cubes) before you add.

$\begin{array}{r} 1\,6 \\ +\,2\,7 \\ \hline 4\,3 \\ \hline \end{array}$ ✔

43 ✔
(2)
(Total for Question 19 is 3 marks)

20 The graph shows a cycle journey made by Jiao to pick up a dress from a shop.

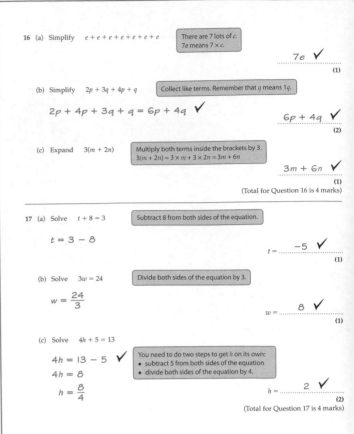

> The graph is flat while Jiao is at the dress shop.
> $\frac{1}{2}$ hour

> This line represents Jiao's journey to the park.

9 km

Distance from home in km
Time in minutes

Jiao cycled from home to the park where she met her friend.
They cycled to the dress shop.
Jiao tried on the dress then cycled back home.

(a) How far is the park from Jiao's home?

7 ✔ km
(1)

(b) How long did Jiao spend in the dress shop?

20 ✔ minutes
(1)

(c) Work out Jiao's speed on her return journey.

> You could also write:
> 9 km travelled in $\frac{1}{2}$ hour
> 18 km travelled in 1 hour.

$9 \div \dfrac{1}{2} = 9 \times 2 = 18$ km/h ✔

18 ✔ km/h
(2)
(Total for Question 20 is 4 marks)

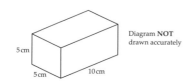

21 The diagram shows a solid block of wood in the shape of a cuboid.

Diagram **NOT** drawn accurately

5 cm

5 cm 10 cm

(a) Work out the total surface area of the cuboid.

$2 \times (5 \times 5) + 2 \times (5 \times 10) + 2 \times (5 \times 10) = 250$

There are 6 faces. Opposite faces have the same area, so you can add them in pairs.

250 ✔ cm²
(1)

Karl has to paint all 6 faces of 50 cuboids.

A can of spray paint covers an area of 3000 cm².

(b) How many cans of paint must Karl buy to paint all the faces?
Show all of your working.

$250 \times 50 = 25 \times 5 \times 10 \times 10$ ✔
$= 12\,500$

You could also work out:
12 500 ÷ 3000 = 4 remainder 500.
Karl needs to buy a whole number of cans of paint, so he needs to buy 5 cans.

4 cans of paint will cover $4 \times 3000 = 12\,000$ cm²
5 cans of paint will cover $5 \times 3000 = 15\,000$ cm² ✔

5 cans ✔
(3)
(Total for Question 21 is 4 marks)

22 Tania and Sebastian receive £60 from their parents.

They share the money in the same ratio as their ages.
Tania is 10 and Sebastian is 14

(a) Write the ratio of their ages Tania : Sebastian in its simplest form.

5 : 7 ✔
(1)

(b) Work out how much money Sebastian got.

$5 + 7 = 12$
$60 \div 12 = 5$ ✔
$7 \times 5 = 35$

There are 12 parts in the ratio in total. So each part is worth £60 ÷ 12 = £5. Sebastian's part of the ratio is 7, so he receives 7 × £5 = £35.

£ 35 ✔
(2)
(Total for Question 22 is 3 marks)

23 (a) Write the number 2.7098 correct to 3 decimal places.

Remember to write the zero in the third decimal place.

2.710 ✔
(1)

(b) Given that $\dfrac{35 \times 5.4}{42} = 4.5$

work out the value of $\dfrac{350 \times 54}{4.2}$

$\dfrac{350 \times 54}{4.2} = \dfrac{35 \times 10 \times 5.4 \times 10}{42 \div 10} = 4.5 \times 1000$ ✔

Both numbers on top of the fraction have been multiplied by 10 and the number on the bottom of the fraction has been divided by 10. So the answer is multiplied by 1000.

4500 ✔
(2)
(Total for Question 23 is 3 marks)

*24 The table below shows details of two companies offering 18-month mobile phone contracts.

Company	Monthly charge	Picture messaging
M-Link	First 6 months FREE, then £25 per month	15p each
Air Talk	£20 per month	FREE

Michelle wants to sign up for an 18-month contract.

She sends 20 picture messages each month.

Michelle wants to pay the least amount of money for her contract.

Which company contract would you advise Michelle to sign up to?
You must show all your working.

Work out the total cost with each company, then write a sentence saying which company Michelle should sign up with.

Air Talk
$18 \times 20 = 360$ ✔
Total cost = £360

You can work out 18 × 20 mentally in two steps:
18 × 2 = 36
36 × 10 = 360

M-Link
$18 - 6 = 12$
$12 \times 25 = 300$
Monthly charge = £300
$18 \times 20 = 360$

```
    360
  ×  15
  1800
  3600
  5400
     1
```

For M-link, work out how many picture messages Michelle will use in total (18 × 20). Each one costs 15p so multiply the result by 15 to work out the total cost in pence. You can use a written method.

Cost of picture messages = 5400p = £54 ✔
Total cost = £300 + £54 = £354 ✔
Michelle should sign up with M-link as it is cheaper. ✔
(Total for Question 24 is 4 marks)

25 The scatter graph shows information about some machinists making jeans.
It shows the number of months each machinist has been working and the number of errors they made during the last month.

(a) What type of correlation does the scatter graph show?

Negative correlation ✔
(1)

A machinist who had been working for 7 months was also checked.

(b) Estimate the number of errors he made during the last month.

Draw a line of best fit on the scatter graph. Read up from 7 on the horizontal axis to your line of best fit, then across to the vertical axis. Your answer will depend on how you've drawn your line of best fit. An acceptable answer would be in the range of 8–11.

9 ✔
(2)
(Total for Question 25 is 3 marks)

26 Here is the recipe Jackie uses for glazing her pots.

> 210 m*l* red
> 450 m*l* light yellow
> 360 m*l* dark yellow
> 480 m*l* white

(a) What volume of glazing does this recipe make?

$$210$$
$$450$$
$$360$$
$$+ \ 480$$
$$\underline{1500}$$
$$\scriptstyle 1 \ 2$$

> Add together the volumes of the ingredients to find the total volume.

............1500............ m*l* ✓ **(1)**

Jackie needs to make only 1 litre of the glazing.

(b) How much of each colour will she need?

<u>Red</u>
$210 ÷ 3 = 70$
$70 × 2 = 140$ ✓

<u>Light yellow</u>
$450 ÷ 3 = 150$
$150 × 2 = 300$

<u>Dark yellow</u>
$360 ÷ 3 = 120$
$120 × 2 = 240$

<u>White</u>
$480 ÷ 3 = 160$
$160 × 2 = 320$

> 1 litre is $\frac{2}{3}$ of 1500 m*l*. This means you need to multiply the amount of each ingredient by $\frac{2}{3}$.
> To multiply by $\frac{2}{3}$ you divide by 3 then multiply by 2.

<u>Check</u>
$$140$$
$$300$$
$$240$$
$$+ \ 320$$
$$\underline{1000}$$
$$\scriptstyle 1 \ 1$$

> Check that the four new quantities add up to 1 litre, or 1000 m*l*.

............140............ m*l* red
............300............ m*l* light yellow ✓
............240............ m*l* dark yellow
............320............ m*l* white ✓ **(3)**

(Total for Question 26 is 4 marks)

22

---

*27

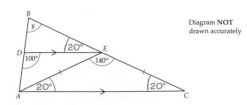

Diagram **NOT** drawn accurately

ABC is a triangle.
DE is parallel to *AC*.

Angle *AEC* = 140°.
Angle *ADE* = 100°.
AE = *EC*.

Work out the value of *y*.
Give reasons for your answer.

EAC is an isosceles triangle.
$\angle EAC = \angle ECA = (180° - 140°) ÷ 2 = 40° ÷ 2 = 20°$ ✓
Base angles of an isosceles triangle are equal.

$\angle BED = 20°$ ✓
Corresponding angles on parallel lines are equal.

$y = 100° - 20° = 80°$ ✓ ✓
Exterior angle of a triangle equals sum of two opposite interior angles. ✓

> There is more than one way to answer this question. Make sure that you give a reason for each step of your working, and write any angles you have worked out on the diagram. Some of the other reasons you could use to answer this question are:
> • angles on a straight line add up to 180°
> • angles in a triangle add up to 180°
> • alternate angles on parallel lines are equal
> • allied (supplementary) angles on parallel lines add up to 180°.

(Total for Question 27 is 5 marks)

---

28 Joel is conducting a survey to find out how many cans of fizzy drink his friends drink. He decides to use a questionnaire.

Write down a suitable question he could use in his survey.

How many cans of fizzy drink do you drink each week? ✓ ✓

☐ None
☐ 1–2
☐ 3–5
☐ More than 5 ✓

> Make sure that:
> • your question gives a time frame
> • your response boxes don't overlap
> • your response boxes have options for all possible answers.

(Total for Question 28 is 3 marks)

24

---

29 Here is a diagram of a parallelogram and a rectangle.

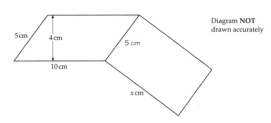

Diagram **NOT** drawn accurately

The parallelogram has the same area as the rectangle.

Work out the length *x*.

Area of parallelogram = $10 × 4 = 40 \text{ cm}^2$ ✓
Area of rectangle = $5 × x$

> Area of a parallelogram = base × vertical height
> You need to remember this formula – it's not given on the formula sheet.

$5x = 40$
$x = 8$ ✓

............8............ ✓ cm
(Total for Question 29 is 3 marks)

TOTAL FOR PAPER IS 100 MARKS

1 (a) Write down the number **seven thousand and thirty-two** in figures.

7032 ✓
(1)

(b) Write down the value of the digit **7** in the number 27 206

> The 7 is in the thousands place.
> You could also write 7 thousands or seven thousands.

7000 ✓
(1)

(c) Write 2453 to the nearest hundred.

> Look at the digit in the tens place. It is a 5 so round up.

2500 ✓
(1)

(Total for Question 1 is 3 marks)

2 $M = 5a - b$

$a = 7.7$
$b = 5.3$

Work out the value of M.

✓
$M = 5 \times 7.7 - 5.3$
$= 33.2$

> Substitute both values into the formula before you do any calculations.

$M = 33.2$ ✓
(Total for Question 2 is 2 marks)

3 The composite bar chart shows the time, in minutes, Clara and Freddie spent on their homework.

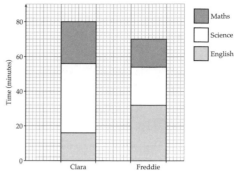

Clara said she spent a greater total time on Maths and English than Freddie.

Is Clara right?
Show all of your working.

> You need to calculate how much time Clara and Freddie each spent on Maths and English, and then write 'yes' or 'no' to answer the question.

<u>Clara</u>
Dark grey (Maths) + Light grey (English) = 24 + 16 = 40
<u>Freddie</u>
Dark grey (Maths) + Light grey (English) = 16 + 32 = 48 ✓

No ✓
(Total for Question 3 is 2 marks)

4 (a) Simplify $2a + 5a$

> $\underbrace{a + a + a + a + a + a + a}_{2a\ +\quad 5a} = 7a$
> $= 7a$

7a ✓
(1)

(b) Simplify $4b - b$

> b means '1 lot of b'.

3b ✓
(1)

(c) Simplify $3c + 2c - 4c$

c ✓
(1)

(Total for Question 4 is 3 marks)

5

A   B   C   D   E

(a) Write down the letter of the shape that is a cone.

D ✓
(1)

(b) How many vertices does shape **C** have?

> Vertices is a mathematical word for corners.

8 ✓
(1)

(c) Write down the mathematical name of shape **E**.

Triangular prism ✓
(1)

(Total for Question 5 is 3 marks)

6 This diagram is drawn accurately.

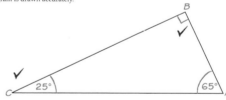

The vertices of this triangle are A, B and C.

Angle $A = 65°$.
Angle $B = 90°$.
Angle $C = 25°$.

Mark the vertices A, B and C and the angles on the diagram.

> Measure each angle with a protractor to work out which is which. Remember to label the 90° angle with a right-angle marker.

(Total for Question 6 is 2 marks)

*7 At a fairground, it costs £2.50 to ride in a dodgem car.
One or two people can ride in each dodgem car.

Darren, Yolanda and Upendra want at least 3 rides each on the dodgem cars.

Work out the total cheapest cost for the children.
You must show all of your working.

D and Y
D and Y
D and U ✓
U and Y ✓
U

> Write down rides until every child has ridden three times. You can use a letter to represent each child.

5 × £2.50 = £12.50

The cheapest cost is £12.50. ✓

(Total for Question 7 is 3 marks)

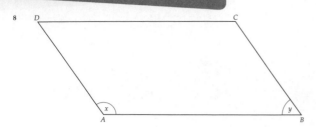

8

(a) Measure the length of *AB*.

> Use a ruler and measure to the nearest mm.
> Make sure you give units with your answer.
> You could also write 113 mm.

11.3 cm ✔
(1)

(b) Measure the size of angle *x*.

125 ✔ °
(1)

(c) Write down the mathematical name for angle *y*.

> Remember these definitions:
> • acute angle: less than 90°
> • obtuse angle: more than 90° and less than 180°
> • reflex angle: more than 180° and less than 360°.

Acute ✔
(1)
(Total for Question 8 is 3 marks)

9 The table gives some information about 5 brands of printer paper.

Brand	Sheets per packet	Weight	Price per 100 sheets	Recycled	Packets per box
Eco-Paper	200	90 g	£0.76	✔	2
SuperStrong	190	100 g	£0.74	✘	8
Paper White	200	90 g	£0.64	✘	6
Copy Write	240	100 g	£0.82	✔	8
Smooth	320	90 g	£0.68	✘	8

(a) Which brand has the lowest price per 100 sheets?

> Find the lowest price in the table.

Paper White ✔
(1)

(b) Which brand with a weight of 90 g has 8 packets per box?

Smooth ✔
(1)

(c) Describe **two** differences between SuperStrong and Copy Write.

1 SuperStrong has fewer sheets per packet. ✔

2 Copy Write is recycled. ✔

> Make sure you use two different properties. If you
> gave reason 1 above, your second reason must
> not be 'Copy Write has more sheets per packet'.

(2)
(Total for Question 9 is 4 marks)

10 Sophie, Mark and Kim raced each other over a fixed distance.
The table shows their times before and after a week of training.

	Sophie	Mark	Kim
Time before training (seconds)	62.30	85.50	58.00
Time after training (seconds)	58.75	81.20	56.25

Sophie aimed to reduce her running time by 3.5 seconds.

(a) Did Sophie achieve her goal?
Show all of your working.

62.3 − 58.75 = 3.55 ✔

> Subtract Sophie's time after training from her
> time before training. She has reduced her time
> by 3.55 seconds, which is more than 3.5 seconds.

Yes ✔
(2)

(b) Who reduced their running time the most?
Show all of your working.

Mark
85.5 − 81.2 = 4.3 ✔

> Work out how much Mark and Kim have
> improved their times, then write down the
> runner with the largest reduction.
> Remember to include Sophie's
> improvement when comparing the results.

Kim
58 − 56.25 = 1.75 ✔

Mark ✔
(3)
(Total for Question 10 is 5 marks)

11 Zoe's colleagues gave her a £200 gift voucher for the online shop Photo Plus.

The table below shows prices for prints of photographs.

Size	Standard	Deluxe
30 cm by 20 cm	£24.99	£48.19
40 cm by 30 cm	£43.99	£55.99
61 cm by 40 cm	£51.49	£72.49
Hanging clip 85p	FREE p&p	

Zoe orders the following prints:

1 Deluxe print 40 cm by 30 cm
2 Standard prints 30 cm by 20 cm
1 Standard print 61 cm by 40 cm

Each print needs two hanging clips.

How much money does Zoe have left from her £200 gift voucher?

£55.99 + 2 × £24.99 + £51.49 = £157.46 ✔
4 × 2 × £0.85 = £6.80 ✔
£157.46 + £6.80 = £164.26
£200 − £164.26 = £35.74
✔

> Write down all your working, and remember
> to subtract the total cost from £200 at the end
> to work out how much money Zoe has left.

£ 35.74 ✔
(Total for Question 11 is 4 marks)

12

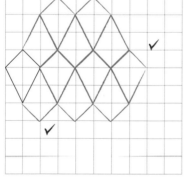

(a) Which shape is a quadrilateral with only one pair of parallel sides?

Shape **F** is a trapezium.

F ✓
(1)

(b) How many lines of symmetry does shape **A** have?

Shape **A** is a square.

4 ✓
(1)

(c) Which shape is a triangle with an obtuse angle?

An obtuse angle is larger than 90° and smaller than 180°.

B ✓
(1)

(d) What is the order of rotational symmetry of shape **G**?

Shape **G** will fit over itself twice when it is rotated through 360°. You can use tracing paper to work out the order of rotational symmetry of a shape.

2 ✓
(1)
(Total for Question 12 is 4 marks)

34

13 Jayden found these coins down the back of his sofa.

10p 5p 1p 1p 10p 5p 2p 2p 2p 20p
1p 1p 10p 20p 2p 2p 1p 20p 5p 10p
5p 20p 1p 1p 20p 2p 1p 1p 20p 10p

(a) Complete the frequency table for the information in the list.

Coin value	Tally	Frequency
1p	|||| ||||	9
2p	||||		6 ✓
5p	||||	4
10p	||||	5
20p	||||		6

✓
(2)

1p and 2p coins are copper.
5p, 10p and 20p coins are silver.

Cross out each value as you tally it. Check that the total of your frequencies is the same as the total number of coins: 9 + 6 + 4 + 5 + 6 = 30 ✓

(b) Work out the difference between the total value of the copper coins and the total value of the silver coins that Jayden found.

Copper coins

$9 \times 1 + 6 \times 2 = 9 + 12 = 21p$

Silver coins

$4 \times 5 + 5 \times 10 + 6 \times 20 = 20 + 50 + 120 = 190p$ ✓

$190 - 21 = 169p = £1.69$ Convert 169p to £1.69.
✓

£ 1.69 ✓
(3)
(Total for Question 13 is 5 marks)

35

14

(a) What is the mathematical name of the quadrilateral drawn on the grid?

Kite ✓
(1)

Use rotations and translations to tessellate the shape. There should be no gaps and no overlaps.

(b) On the grid, show how the quadrilateral tessellates.
You should draw at least 6 shapes.

(2)
(Total for Question 14 is 3 marks)

15 Rosario recorded the outside temperature at different times during the weekend.

Time	6 am	Noon	6 pm	Midnight
Saturday	−2 °C	8 °C	2 °C	−5 °C
Sunday	−4 °C	9 °C	0 °C	−8 °C

(a) What was the lowest recorded temperature?

The lowest temperature was recorded at midnight on Sunday.

−8 ✓ °C
(1)

(b) When was the recorded temperature 6 °C lower than the temperature at 6 pm on Saturday?

$2 - 6 = -4$

6 am on Sunday ✓
(1)

(c) What is the difference between the temperature at noon on Sunday and at midnight on Saturday?

$9 - -5 = 9 + 5 = 14$ Subtracting a negative number is the same as adding a positive number.

14 ✓ °C
(1)
(Total for Question 15 is 3 marks)

16 (a) Factorise $6a + 8b$

Check by multiplying out:
$2(3a + 4b) = 2 \times 3a + 2 \times 4b = 6a + 8b$ ✓

$2(3a + 4b)$ ✓
(1)

(b) Factorise completely $3ab - 9a^2$

You need to write the largest possible factor outside the brackets:
$a(3b - 9a) \rightarrow$ partly factorised ✗
$3(ab - 3a^2) \rightarrow$ partly factorised ✗
$3a(b - 3a) \rightarrow$ completely factorised ✓

$3a(b - 3a)$ ✓✓
(2)
(Total for Question 16 is 3 marks)

17 This shape is made from a rectangle and a triangle.

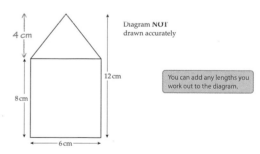

4 cm

Diagram **NOT** drawn accurately

12 cm

You can add any lengths you work out to the diagram.

8 cm

6 cm

Work out the area of the shape.

$12 - 8 = 4$ ✓

Rectangle

$6 \times 8 = 48$

You can work out the area of the triangle and the rectangle then add them together. Remember to show your working clearly.

Triangle

$\frac{1}{2} \times 6 \times 4 = 12$ ✓

Area of a triangle $= \frac{1}{2} \times$ base $\times$ vertical height

Total area $= 48 + 12 = 60$

60 ✓ cm^2
(Total for Question 17 is 3 marks)

37

135

*18 Helen bought 36 m of climbing rope for £104.40
Jamie bought 45 m of the same type of climbing rope for £123.32

Who got the better value?
Give reasons for your answer.

Helen
104.4 ÷ 36 = 2.90 ✓
£2.90 per metre

Jamie
123.32 ÷ 45 = 2.7404... ✓
£2.74 per metre ✓ ✓

Jamie got the better value. ✓

> For each person divide the cost by the length of the rope to work out the cost per metre. Compare the costs per metre and write down who got the better value.

> This question has a star. This means you need to use the correct units, show all your working neatly, and write down who got the better value.

(Total for Question 18 is 4 marks)

---

*19 Barney wants to travel from Valdosta to Atlanta in the USA.

He measures the distance between Valdosta and Atlanta on the map to be 14 cm.
The map has a scale of 1 cm to 20 miles.

His car averages 35 miles per gallon of petrol.
Petrol costs $4.59 per gallon.
His tank is empty when he sets out from Valdosta.

Barney has $25 cash in his wallet.

Will he have enough money for the journey?
Show all of your working.

Real distance from Valdosta to Atlanta
14 × 20 = 280 miles ✓

Number of gallons required
280 ÷ 35 = 8

Cost of fuel
8 × $4.59 = $36.72 ✓

No. He only has $25 and he needs $36.72. ✓
✓

> There are lots of steps so work carefully:
> • use the map scale to work out the real-life distance from Valdosta to Atlanta
> • divide by 35 to work out how many gallons of petrol he needs
> • multiply by $4.59 to work out the total cost
> • compare this to $25 and write a conclusion.

(Total for Question 19 is 4 marks)

---

20 You can use this graph to change between gallons and litres.

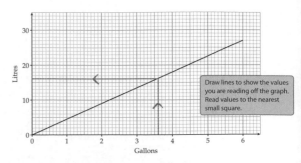

> Draw lines to show the values you are reading off the graph. Read values to the nearest small square.

The petrol tank of a motorcycle has a capacity of 3.6 gallons.

(a) How many litres of petrol are needed to fill the tank of the motorcycle?

16 ✓ litres
(1)

A garage is selling a 5 gallon drum of oil for the same price as a 25 litre drum of oil.

(b) Which of the drums is the better value?
Show your working.

5 × 4.5 = 22.5

> Use the graph, or use 1 gallon = 4.5 litres. 5 gallons = 22.5 litres so the 25 litre drum is better value.

25 litre drum ✓
(1)

Royce filled his tractor with 10 pints of oil from a new 5 gallon drum.

1 gallon = 8 pints

(c) Estimate the number of litres of oil left in the drum.

10 pints = $1\frac{1}{4}$ gallons

> 10 pints = 1 gallon and 2 pints = $1\frac{2}{8}$ gallons = $1\frac{1}{4}$ gallons

$5 - 1\frac{1}{4} = 3\frac{3}{4}$ ✓

> Use the graph, or use 1 gallon = 4.5 litres.

$3\frac{3}{4} \times 4.5 = 16.875$

17 ✓ litres
(2)
(Total for Question 20 is 4 marks)

---

21 Pete recorded these prices per kg for different cheeses.

£7.50 £11.40 £16.25 £8.35 £12.80 £15.45 £9.00 £6.45

(a) Work out the median price.

£6.45, £7.50, £8.35, (£9.00, £11.40,) £12.80, £15.45, £16.25

$\frac{9 + 11.4}{2} = \frac{20.4}{2} = 10.2$ ✓

> Write the values in order of size, crossing each one off as you go. There are 8 data values so the median is half way between the 4th and 5th values.

£ 10.20 ✓
(2)

(b) Work out the mean price.

6.45 + 7.5 + 8.35 + 9 + 11.4 + 12.8 + 15.45 + 16.25 = 87.2 ✓
87.2 ÷ 8 = 10.9

> Add together the data values, then divide by 8. Give your answer in £ to 2 decimal places.

£ 10.90 ✓
(2)

(c) Work out the range.

16.25 − 6.45 = 9.8

> Range = largest value − smallest value

£ 9.80 ✓
(1)
(Total for Question 21 is 5 marks)

---

22 Marin placed 3 red balls and 2 blue balls inside a bag.

She asked a friend to choose one of the balls without looking.

(a) What is the probability that her friend chose a blue ball?

> There are 2 successful outcomes and 5 possible outcomes. You can give your answer as $\frac{2}{5}$ or 0.4.

$\frac{2}{5}$ ✓ ✓
(2)

Marin wants to change the probability of choosing a blue ball to 0.2 by adding more red balls to the bag.

(b) How many red balls does she need to add to the bag?

$0.2 = \frac{2}{10}$ ✓
10 − 5 = 5

> There are still only 2 blue balls in the bag. $0.2 = \frac{2}{10}$ so there need to be 10 balls in the bag in total.

> Check: there are now 2 blue balls and 8 red balls in the bag, so P(Blue) = $\frac{2}{10}$ = 0.2. ✓

5 ✓
(2)
(Total for Question 22 is 4 marks)

---

23 The exterior angle of a regular polygon is 40°.

(a) Work out the number of sides the polygon has.

360 ÷ 40 = 9 ✓

> The exterior angles of a polygon add up to 360°. A regular polygon has equal angles so divide 360° by 40°.

9 ✓
(2)

This diagram shows a regular pentagon.

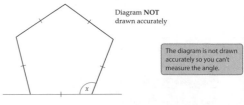

Diagram **NOT** drawn accurately

> The diagram is not drawn accurately so you can't measure the angle.

(b) Find the size of the interior angle x.
You must show your working.

> Each exterior angle is equal to 360° ÷ 5 = 72°. The angles on a straight line add up to 180°, so the interior angle is 180° − 72° = 108°.

360 ÷ 5 = 72 ✓
180 − 72 = 108

108 ✓ °
(2)
(Total for Question 23 is 4 marks)

24 Use your calculator to find the value of $\frac{174}{6.2 - \sqrt{18}}$.

Write your answer correct to 3 significant figures. ✓

> Show what the bottom of the fraction comes to in your working. You can check your answer by entering it into the calculator in one go.

$174 \div 1.957\,359\,313 = 88.89527786$ ✓

> Write down all the digits from your calculator display before you round your answer.

88.9 ✓

(Total for Question 24 is 3 marks)

***25** Here is a diagram of a farmer's field.

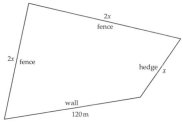

Diagram **NOT** drawn accurately

The perimeter of the field is 520 m.

The farmer wants to replace the fence with new wire.

He has 300 m of wire.
There is fencing along 2 edges.

Does the farmer have enough wire?
You must show your working.

$2x + 2x + x + 120 = 520$ ✓

$5x + 120 = 520$

$5x = 400$

$x = 80$ ✓

> Use the information in the question to write an equation. Solve your equation to find x.

$2x + 2x = 4x$

$= 4 \times 80$

$= 320$ ✓

> Work out the length of the fence, and compare this to the amount of wire the farmer has. Make sure you show all your working and answer the question 'yes' or 'no'.

No. The farmer needs 320 m of wire and only has 300 m. ✓

(Total for Question 25 is 4 marks)

---

26 (a) The number x satisfies the inequality $3 < x \leqslant 7$

Show the inequality on the number line. ✓

> Use a closed circle for ⩽ or ⩾ and an open circle for < or >.

(1)

(b) (i) Solve the inequality

$$4n + 7 \geqslant 21$$

$4n + 7 \geqslant 21$

$4n \geqslant 14$ ✓

$n \geqslant 3.5$

> Your answer should have the letter on its own on one side of the inequality and a number on the other side.

$n \geqslant 3.5$ ✓

(2)

n is an integer.

(ii) Write down the smallest possible value of n.

4 ✓

(1)

(Total for Question 26 is 4 marks)

27

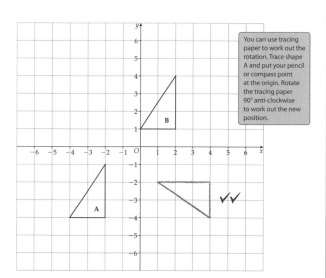

> You can use tracing paper to work out the rotation. Trace shape A and put your pencil or compass point at the origin. Rotate the tracing paper 90° anti-clockwise to work out the new position.

(a) Rotate triangle **A** 90° anti-clockwise about the origin.

(2)

(b) Fully describe the transformation that maps triangle **A** onto triangle **B**.

Translation ✓ by $\begin{pmatrix} 4 \\ 5 \end{pmatrix}$ ✓

(2)

(Total for Question 27 is 4 marks)

> You must use a vector to describe a translation. The top number describes the horizontal movement and the bottom number describes the vertical movement.
> • Positive numbers: movement right or up.
> • Negative numbers: movement left or down.

---

28 Two shops are selling the same jacket in the January sales.

Suits You
Jacket
£140 plus VAT @ 20%

Smarts
Jacket
£180 incl. VAT
12% off marked price

In which shop is the jacket cheaper?
Show all of your working.

<u>Suits You</u>

$\frac{20}{100} \times 140 = 28$ ✓

$140 + 28 = 168$ ✓

<u>Smarts</u>

$\frac{12}{100} \times 180 = 21.6$ ✓

$180 - 21.6 = 158.4$ ✓

> Increase £140 by 20% and reduce £180 by 12%, then compare the answers.
> You could also use multipliers:
> • the multiplier for a 20% increase is 1.2
> • the multiplier for a 12% decrease is 0.88.

> Make sure you answer the question by writing down which shop is cheaper.

Smarts ✓

(Total for Question 28 is 5 marks)

TOTAL FOR PAPER IS 100 MARKS

1 (a) Toby measures this length of wood.

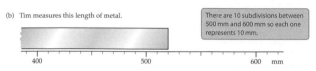

> Work out what each small subdivision represents. There are 10 subdivisions between 7 cm and 8 cm so each one represents 0.1 cm.

Write down the length of the wood.

.... 7.8 ✔ cm

(1)

(b) Tim measures this length of metal.

> There are 10 subdivisions between 500 mm and 600 mm so each one represents 10 mm.

Write down the length of the metal.

.... 520 ✔ mm

(1)

(c) Here is part of the scale on a set of weighing scales.

Use the scale to find an estimate for

(i) 5 kg in pounds

> 10 kg = 22 pounds so 5 kg = 11 pounds

.... 11 ✔ pounds

(1)

(ii) 16 pounds in kilograms.

> Find 16 pounds on the right-hand scale. It is about a quarter of the way between 7 kg and 8 kg, so 7.25 kg is a good estimate.

.... 7.25 ✔ kilograms

(1)

(Total for Question 1 is 4 marks)

46

---

2 (a) A shop sold 63 cans on Monday, 134 cans on Tuesday and 55 cans on Wednesday.

How many cans will the shop need to order to replace the cans sold?

$$\begin{array}{r} 63 \\ 134 \\ + \ 55 \\ \hline 252 \\ \hline \end{array}$$ ✔

> Use column addition, and make sure you line up digits with the same place value.

.... 252 ✔

(2)

(b) A shop has 80 bottles of perfume in stock.
The shop then sells 23 bottles of perfume.

How many bottles of perfume are now in stock?

> If you use a mental method make sure you write down the calculation you are working out.

$$80 - 23 = 60 - 3 = 57$$ ✔

.... 57 ✔

(2)

(Total for Question 2 is 4 marks)

3 Write down the name of each of these 3-D solids.

(a)   (b)   (c)

cuboid ✔   cone ✔   cylinder ✔

(Total for Question 3 is 3 marks)

---

4 (a) Work out 24×100

> The digits move two places to the left on a place value diagram.

.... 2400 ✔

(1)

(b) Work out $7 + 4 + 9 + 4 + 2 + 8 + 1 + 3$

.... 38 ✔

(1)

(c) Work out $3003 - 404$

$$\begin{array}{r} 3003 \\ - \ 404 \\ \hline 2599 \\ \hline \end{array}$$ ✔

> You can use any method you like, but remember to show all your working.

.... 2599 ✔

(2)

(Total for Question 4 is 4 marks)

5 The table gives information about six mobile phones

Phone	Cost	Recharge time (minutes)	Weight (grams)	4G-compatible
C9090	£89.50	90	90	
D404	£175	210	121	✔
G103	£205	160	104	✔
G405	£39.95	85	83	
X12	£100	160	87	
X4A	£275	180	111	✔

(a) Which phone is the heaviest?

.... D404 ✔

(1)

(b) Which phones cost less than £150?

.... C9090, G405 and X12 ✔

> Look at the cost column. There are 3 phones which cost less than £150. Make sure you write them all.

(1)

(c) Which phone is 4G-compatible **and** has a recharge time of 160 minutes?

> Only look at the phones which have a tick in the last column.

.... G103 ✔

(1)

(Total for Question 5 is 3 marks)

48

---

6 Here is a list of numbers.

$$2 \quad 7 \quad 9 \quad 11 \quad 12 \quad 42 \quad 45$$

From the list,

(a) write down an even number greater than 10

> You could also write 42.

.... 12 ✔

(1)

(b) write down a square number

> $3^2 = 9$

.... 9 ✔

(1)

(c) write down a multiple of 4

> It's OK to use the same number twice as long as it is correct.

.... 12 ✔

(1)

(d) write down a factor of 6

> The factors of 6 are 1, 2, 3 and 6, so 2 is the only option.

.... 2 ✔

(1)

(Total for Question 6 is 4 marks)

7 The diagram shows information about the height of a chair.
It also shows the height of the seat of the chair from the floor.

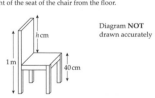

Diagram **NOT** drawn accurately

What is the height, h, of the back of the chair?

$$1 \text{ m} = 100 \text{ cm}$$ ✔

$$h = 100 \text{ cm} - 40 \text{ cm}$$
$$= 60 \text{ cm}$$

> Convert the total height of the chair into cm so that both measurements are in the same units (cm). Then subtract the height of the seat from the total height of the chair.

.... 60 ✔ cm

(Total for Question 7 is 2 marks)

8 The diagram shows a circle, centre O.

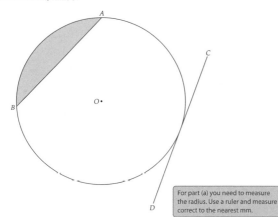

For part (a) you need to measure the radius. Use a ruler and measure correct to the nearest mm.

(a) Write down the length of the radius of the circle.

............4.8..✔........ cm
(1)

(b) What is the mathematical name of the line *CD*?

.......Tangent..✔.........
(1)

(c) What is the mathematical name of the straight line *AB*?

.......Chord..✔.........
(1)

(d) What is the mathematical name of the curved line *AB*?

.......Arc..✔.........
(1)

(e) What is the mathematical name of the shaded area?

.......Segment..✔.........
(1)

A chord divides a circle into two segments. You could also write 'minor segment' as this is the smaller of the two segments.

(Total for Question 8 is 5 marks)

9 Jasmine's pay is worked out using this rule.

Pay = £8 × number of hours worked

On Monday Jasmine works for 4 hours.

You multiply hours worked by 8 to work out pay in pounds.

(a) Work out her pay for Monday.

$8 × 4 = 32$ ✔

£............32..✔........
(2)

On Tuesday Jasmine's pay is £52

(b) How many hours does she work on Tuesday?

$8\overline{)52.{}^40}$ ✔
6.5

The inverse operation of × 8 is ÷ 8. So divide £52 by 8 to work out how many hours Jasmine worked. Remember your answer doesn't have to be a whole number.

............6.5..✔........ hours
(2)

(Total for Question 9 is 4 marks)

10 Find the value of $3x + 5y$ when $x = 3$ and $y = 4$

$3 × 3 + 5 × 4 = 9 + 20$ ✔
$= 29$

$3x$ means $3 × x$. Substitute the values for x and y into the expression then work out its value. Remember BIDMAS – do the Multiplication before the Addition.

............29..✔........
(Total for Question 10 is 2 marks)

11 Aden buys

  one pineapple costing £1.55
  one mango costing 99p
  two melons.

Aden pays with a £5 note.
He gets 20p change.

Work out the cost of **one** melon.

$1.55 + 0.99 = 2.54$

You can add 0.99 by adding 1, then subtracting 0.01.

$5 - 0.2 = 4.8$

Aden gets 20p change from £5.
$5 - 0.2 = 4.8$ so in total he pays £4.80.

$\begin{array}{r} 4.\overset{7}{\cancel{8}}{}^10 \\ -2.54 \\ \hline 2.26 \end{array}$ ✔

Work in pence or pounds, but not both.

If all the digits in a number are even, you can divide by 2 by halving each digit.

$2.26 ÷ 2 = 1.13$ ✔

£............1.13..✔........
(Total for Question 11 is 3 marks)

12 In a sale, full prices are reduced by $\frac{1}{3}$

The full price of a crash helmet is £180

What is the sale price of the crash helmet?

$180 ÷ 3 = 60$ ✔
$180 - 60 = 120$ ✔

Divide by 3 to work out $\frac{1}{3}$ of £180.
$18 ÷ 3 = 6$ so $180 ÷ 3 = 60$

The price is reduced, so subtract $\frac{1}{3}$ from the original price.

£............120..✔........
(Total for Question 12 is 3 marks)

*13 Tammy makes and sells paperweights.
The paperweights are posted in boxes in the shape of a cuboid.

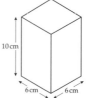

Diagram **NOT** drawn accurately

Tammy sketches five designs for the net of the box.

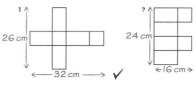

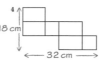

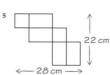

All the short sides are 6 cm and all the long sides are 10 cm. Work out the total width and height of each design.

Tammy wants her design to fit on a 25 cm × 25 cm square card.

Which design should Tammy choose?
Give reasons for your answer.
Give reasons why she should not choose the other designs.

Design 3 ✔
Designs 1, 4 and 5 will not fit.
Design 2 is not the net of a cuboid. ✔

The net needs to fit on the paper and fold up to make the cuboid. Design 2 will fit, but it is not the net of a cuboid, so it will not fold up to make Tammy's box.

(Total for Question 13 is 4 marks)

51

53

14 This is a conversion graph for British pounds (£) and Australian dollars ($).

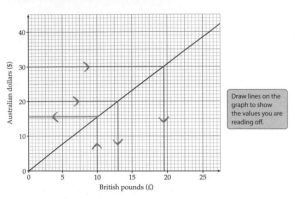

(a) Use the conversion graph to change:
(i) 10 British pounds (£) to Australian dollars ($)

| Read up from £10 to the graph, then across to the vertical axis. |

$ ....15.50.... ✔
(1)

(ii) 20 Australian dollars ($) to British pounds (£).

£ ....13.00.... ✔
(1)

(b) Change 90 Australian dollars ($) into British pounds (£).

| The graph doesn't go up to $90. You can read other values off the graph to work out $90 in pounds. |

$30 = £19.50 ✔
3 × 19.50 = 58.50 | $90 = 3 × $30 |
$90 = £58.50

£ ....58.50.... ✔
(2)
(Total for Question 14 is 4 marks)

54

---

15 The bar chart shows the number of job applications Susan sent during one week.

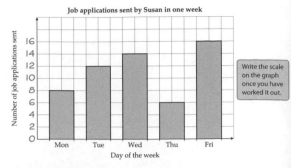

| Write the scale on the graph once you have worked it out. |

On Tuesday Susan sent 12 job applications.

How many job applications did Susan send altogether during this week?
You must show your working.

12 ÷ 6 = 2 ✔

| You need to work out the scale on the vertical axis. The bar for Tuesday is 6 squares high and represents 12 job applications, so each square represents 2 job applications. |

8 + 12 + 14 + 6 + 16 = 56
✔   ✔   ✔

....56.... ✔
(Total for Question 15 is 5 marks)

---

16 Work out   342 × 12

```
    342
×    12
  ─────
    684  ✔
   3420  ✔
  ─────
   4104
    1 1
```

| You could also use partitioning:
342 × 10 = 3420
342 × 2 = 684
342 × 12 = 4104 |

....4104.... ✔
(Total for Question 16 is 3 marks)

17 (a) Write $\frac{3}{4}$ as a decimal.

| Try to learn the most common fraction-to-decimal conversions. |

....0.75.... ✔
(1)

(b) Simplify $\frac{20}{24}$
Give your answer in its simplest form.

| 20 and 24 have a common factor of 4, so divide top and bottom by 4. |

$\frac{5}{6}$ ✔
(1)

(c) Daniel says $\frac{3}{5}$ is larger than $\frac{2}{3}$

Is he right?
Explain your answer.

| To compare fractions they have to have the same denominator. Write equivalent fractions with denominator 15. |

$\frac{3}{5} = \frac{9}{15}$ ✔

$\frac{2}{3} = \frac{10}{15}$ ✔

| Remember to write a conclusion and answer the question. |

So $\frac{2}{3}$ is larger. Daniel is wrong. ✔

(3)
(Total for Question 17 is 5 marks)

---

18 Here is part of a train timetable from Milford Haven to Manchester.

Milford Haven to Manchester

Milford Haven	06 00	07 05	09 08	11 08	13 08
Swansea	07 45	08 55	10 55	12 54	14 55
Cardiff	08 50	10 05	12 05	14 05	15 50
Hereford	09 51	11 06	13 06	15 06	16 53
Shrewsbury	10 53	11 58	13 58	15 58	17 50
Manchester	12 15	13 15	15 15	17 14	19 15

A train leaves Milford Haven at 06 00

(a) At what time should it arrive in Manchester?

....12 15.... ✔
(1)

Another train leaves Cardiff at 15 50

(b) Work out how many minutes this train should take to go from Cardiff to Hereford.

10 + 53 = 63 | Count on from 15 50 to 16 53 in two steps:
+10 mins   +53 mins
15 50 ⟶ 16 00 ⟶ 16 53 |

....63.... ✔
(1)

Lynn lives in Milford Haven.

She has a meeting in Shrewsbury at 14 00
When Lynn arrives in Shrewsbury it takes 20 minutes to travel to her meeting.

(c) What is the time of the latest train she can take from Milford Haven to be on time for her meeting?

| Lynn can't catch the 09 08 train because it gets in to Shrewsbury at 13 58. It takes her 20 minutes to get to her meeting from the station, so she wouldn't be there until 14 18. |

....07 05.... ✔
(1)
(Total for Question 18 is 3 marks)

56

19 The Angel of the North is a statue.
    The statue is 20 m tall.

Penny makes a model of the statue.
She uses a scale of 1 : 25

What is the height of the model of the statue?
Give your answer in centimetres.

20 × 100 = 2000 ✔
2000 ÷ 25 = 80
                    ✔

> You have to give your answer in cm, so multiply 20 m by 100 to convert into cm. Then divide by 25 to work out the height of the model.

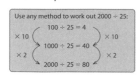

Use any method to work out 2000 ÷ 25:
```
            100 ÷ 25 = 4
  × 10    ⟨              ⟩  × 10
            1000 ÷ 25 = 40
  × 2     ⟨              ⟩  × 2
            2000 ÷ 25 = 80
```

80 ✔ cm
....
(Total for Question 19 is 3 marks)

*20 Emir works 120 hours per month.
    He is paid £8 per hour.

His rent is £400 per month.

Emir gets a pay rise of 5%.

His rent increases to £430 per month.

Is Emir better off or worse off each month?
You must show your working.

Before
120 × 8 = 960
960 − 400 = 560 ✔
            ✔

> 12 × 8 = 96, so 120 × 8 = 960

> Work out how much money Emir has after he pays his rent. Compare the amounts before and after his pay rise and write a conclusion.

After
10% of 960 = 96
5% of 960 = 48
960 + 48 = 1008

> To find 5% of £960 find 10% then divide it by 2. You need to increase £960 by 5% so add £48 on to £960.

$\overset{9}{1}\overset{}{0}\overset{1}{0}8$
− 430 ✔
  _____
   578 ✔

> You could also work out Emir's extra monthly pay and compare that with his £30 rent increase.

£578 is more than £560 so he is better off after the pay rise. ✔

(Total for Question 20 is 5 marks)

*21 A fair three-sided spinner has sections labelled 1, 2 and 4
    A fair four-sided dice has faces labelled 1, 2, 3 and 4

The spinner is spun and the dice is rolled at the same time.
The number the spinner lands on is added to the number shown on the dice to give
a total score.

Work out the probability that the total score is less than 5

Spinner

		1	2	4
	1	2	3	5
Dice	2	3	4	6
	3	4	5	7
	4	5	6	8

✔✔

> Draw a sample space diagram to show all the possible outcomes. There are 12 outcomes in total. 5 outcomes have a total score less than 5, so the probability of a total score less than 5 is $\frac{5}{12}$.

$\frac{5}{12}$ ✔
....
(Total for Question 21 is 3 marks)

22 Femke asked 100 adults where they spent their summer holiday.
    Each adult either spent their holiday in the UK or they spent their holiday abroad.

Of the 36 people who spent their holiday in the UK, 26 were men.
35 women asked spent their holiday abroad.

How many more men spent their holiday abroad than in the UK?

	UK	Abroad	Total
M	26	29	55
F	10	35	45
Total	36	64	100

✔✔

> You can use a two-way table to answer this question. Fill in the information given in the question, then use addition and subtraction to work out and fill in the missing values.

29 − 26 = 3
      ✔

3 ✔
....
(Total for Question 22 is 4 marks)

23 (a) Estimate $\sqrt{27}$
        Explain how you got your answer.

5.2 ✔

> This is the non-calculator paper so you can't use trial and improvement. Find a number whose square is close to 27 and use that to make an estimate. An acceptable range would be 5.1–5.3.

Because $5^2 = 25$ so $\sqrt{27}$ will be slightly larger than 5. ✔

(2)

(b) Work out an estimate for $\dfrac{21.4 \times 6.88}{0.52}$

$\dfrac{20 \times 7}{0.5} = \dfrac{140}{0.5} = 280$

> Round all the numbers to 1 significant figure. Make sure you write out the calculation with the rounded values.

280 ✔
....
(3)
(Total for Question 23 is 5 marks)

58

59

60

61

*24

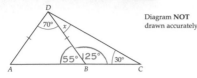

Diagram **NOT** drawn accurately

ABC is a straight line.
BD = *AD*.
Angle *BCD* = 30°.
Angle *ADB* = 70°.

Work out the size of the angle marked *x*.
Give reasons for your answer.

$$\frac{180 - 70}{2} = \frac{110}{2} = 55 \quad \checkmark$$

$\angle ABD = 55°$

Base angles in an isosceles triangle are equal. ✓

$180 - 55 = 125$

$\angle DBC = 125°$ ✓

Angles on a straight line add up to 180°.

$180 - 125 - 30 = 25$

$x = 25°$ ✓

Angles in a triangle add up to 180°.

> Write any angles you work out on your diagram, and remember to give reasons for each step of your working.

(Total for Question 24 is 4 marks)

---

25 Sam wanted to find out which holiday destinations are popular with families.
He interviewed people at Luton airport in January.

(a) His sample is biased.
Give two reasons to show his sample is biased.

> You could also say that fewer families are likely to go on holiday in January.

1 He only interviewed people at an airport so he didn't interview people who don't fly. ✓

2 Some destinations (like ski resorts) may be more popular in January. ✓

(2)

(b) Write a suitable question Sam could use to find out which holiday destinations are popular with families.

Which country do you like to go on holiday with your family? ✓

☐ UK
☐ France
☐ Spain
☐ Italy
☐ USA
☐ Other ✓

> Keep your question simple.

> Write at least 4 response boxes and make sure you include a box for 'other' so everyone can tick a box.

(2)
(Total for Question 25 is 4 marks)

---

26 In a restaurant, tables can be placed together for large numbers of people.

The diagram shows chairs arranged around tables.

(a) How many chairs are needed for six tables placed together?

Number of tables (*n*)	1	2	3	4	5	6
Number of chairs	4	6	8	10	12	14

+2 +2 +2 +2 +2 ✓

> Continue the number sequence until you get to 6 tables.

14 ✓

(2)

(b) Find an expression, in terms of *n*, for the number of chairs at *n* tables.

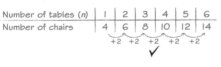

Number of tables (*n*)	1	2	3	4	5	6
Number of chairs	4	6	8	10	12	14
2*n*	2	4	6	8	10	12

✓

> The term-to-term rule is 'add 2'. So the *n*th term will be 2*n* ± □. Compare 2*n* with each term to work out what you need to add or subtract.

$2n + 2$ ✓

(2)
(Total for Question 26 is 4 marks)

---

27 (a) Simplify $y^6 \div y^3$

> $a^m \div a^n = a^{m-n}$

y^3 ✓
(1)

(b) Simplify $3x^3 \times 4x^5$

$3 \times 4 \times x^3 \times x^5$ ✓ $a^m \times a^n = a^{m+n}$

$12x^8$ ✓

(2)
(Total for Question 27 is 3 marks)

TOTAL FOR PAPER IS 100 MARKS

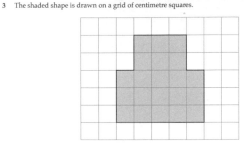

1 (a) Write down the number 3456 in words.

Three thousand four hundred and fifty six ✓

Make sure you don't write any figures.

(1)

(b) Write the number **eight thousand two hundred and six** in figures.

8206 ✓

(1)

(c) Write down the value of the digit **5** in the number 3571

The 5 is in the hundreds place.
You can also write 5 hundred or five hundred.

500 ✓

(1)

(Total for Question 1 is 3 marks)

2 Here are the names of seven rabbits.

Abbi   Pl   Emma   Patch   Gill   Penny   Polly

Sandra picks one rabbit at random.

Circle the correct word that describes the probability that Sandra picks a rabbit that:

(a) has a name that contains four letters

3 out of 7 rabbits' names contain four letters, so the probability is less than evens, but not impossible.

impossible   (unlikely)   evens   likely   certain
                  ✓

(1)

(b) has a name that begins with the letter P

4 out of 7 rabbits' names begin with the letter P, so the probability is greater than evens, but not certain.

impossible   unlikely   evens   (likely)   certain
                                      ✓

(1)

(c) has a name that ends with the letter S.

No rabbits' names end with the letter S, so it is impossible to pick one.

(impossible)   unlikely   evens   likely   certain
      ✓

(1)

(Total for Question 2 is 3 marks)

66

3 The shaded shape is drawn on a grid of centimetre squares.

You can work out the area by counting squares.

(a) (i) Work out the area of the shaded shape.

21 ✓ cm²

(1)

(ii) Work out the perimeter of the shaded shape.

The perimeter is the distance all the way around the shape.

5 + 3 + 1 + 2 + 3 + 2 + 1 + 3 = 20   20 ✓ cm

Add together the lengths of all the sides.

(1)

This is a solid prism made of centimetre cubes.

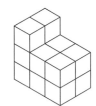

Diagram **NOT** drawn accurately

(b) Work out the volume of the prism.

2 × 7 = 14

Count the number of cm cubes needed to make the shape. Remember to include the cubes you can't see. The shape is a prism so it must have a constant cross-section.

14 ✓ cm³

(1)

(Total for Question 3 is 3 marks)

67

4 Tyson has a £10 note to spend on lemonade.

A bottle of lemonade costs 78p.

He buys as many bottles of lemonade as possible.

Work out how much change Tyson should get.

£10 = 1000p

10 × 78 = 780
11 × 78 = 858
12 × 78 = 936 ✓
13 × 78 = 1014

When working with money, work in pounds or pence but not both.

13 bottles would cost 1014p or £10.14 which is too expensive.

1000 − 936 = 64

Subtract the cost of 12 bottles from 1000p to work out Tyson's change in pence.

64 ✓ p

(Total for Question 4 is 3 marks)

5 The table shows the temperature, in °C, at midday on a winter's day in six towns.

Town	York	Selby	Wakefield	Worksop	Lincoln	Burwell
Temperature (°C)	1	−1	−4	0	−2	−3

(a) Which town
   (i) had the lowest temperature at midday?

Wakefield ✓

−4 °C was the lowest temperature.

(1)

   (ii) had the highest temperature at midday?

York ✓

Write down the name of the town, not the temperature.

(1)

The midday temperature in Sheffield was 5°C higher than the midday temperature in Burwell.

(b) Work out the midday temperature in Sheffield.

−3 + 5 = 2

2 ✓ °C

(1)

(Total for Question 5 is 3 marks)

68

6 (a) What fraction of this shape is shaded?

5 and 8 have no common factors so you can't simplify this fraction.

$\frac{5}{8}$ ✓

(1)

(b) Convert 0.7 to a fraction.

0.7 means 7 tenths or $\frac{7}{10}$

$\frac{7}{10}$ ✓

(1)

(c) What percentage of this shape is shaded?

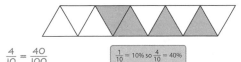

$\frac{4}{10} = \frac{40}{100}$ $\frac{1}{10} = 10\%$ so $\frac{4}{10} = 40\%$

40 ✓ %

(1)

(Total for Question 6 is 3 marks)

69

143

7 Sam made a list of his last 9 test marks.

9   4   5   8   5   5   8   9   10

(a) Write down the mode.

The value 5 occurs 3 times.

5 ✔
(1)

(b) Work out the range.

Range = largest value − smallest value

$10 - 4 = 6$ ✔

6 ✔
(2)

(c) Work out the mean.

$9 + 4 + 5 + 8 + 5 + 5 + 8 + 9 + 10 = 63$
$63 ÷ 9 = 7$ ✔

Add together all the values, then divide by the total number of values, 9.

7 ✔
(2)
(Total for Question 7 is 5 marks)

8 (a) Put these numbers in order, starting with the smallest.

-7 -2 0   4   6

4   6   −2   0   −7

$-7, -2, 0, 4, 6$ ✔
(1)

(b) Put these numbers in order, starting with the smallest.

7.2   7.8   7.25   7.15

Compare the largest place values first. 7.2 has a larger tenths digit than 7.15 so it is larger.

7.2
7.8
7.25
7.15

7.15, 7.2, 7.25, 7.8 ✔
(1)
(Total for Question 8 is 2 marks)

9 (a) Simplify $8a - 3a$

$8a$ means '8 lots of a'.
'8 lots of a' − '3 lots of a' = '5 lots of a'

5a ✔
(1)

(b) Simplify $3b × 3b$

You can multiply in any order. Multiply the number parts then multiply the letter parts.

$3 × 3 × b × b = 9b^2$

$9b^2$ ✔
(1)

(c) Simplify $c^2 + c^2$

$2c^2$ ✔
(1)

(d) Simplify $5d + 4e - 3d + e$

$5d - 3d + 4e + e = 2d + 5e$ ✔

Collect like terms. Remember each term goes with the sign (+ or −) in front of it.

Remember e means '1 lot of e'.

$2d + 5e$ ✔
(2)
(Total for Question 9 is 5 marks)

10 (a) Measure the size of the angle marked x.

Place the cross-hairs of your protractor on the corner of the angle and line up the zero line along one arm. Make sure you choose the scale which starts at 0, and read to the nearest degree.

135 ✔ °
(1)

The diagram shows three angles.

Diagram **NOT** drawn accurately

40° y

(b) (i) Work out the value of y.

The right angle is 90°. All three angles must add up to 180°, so subtract 40° and 90° from 180°.

$180 - 40 - 90 = 50$ ✔

50 ✔ °
(2)

(ii) Give a reason for your answer.

Angles on a straight line add up to 180°. ✔
(1)
(Total for Question 10 is 4 marks)

11 Dianne completes a weekly bar chart that shows the numbers of men and women who gave positive feedback to a supermarket questionnaire.

This is the bar chart for one week.

The bar for men on Friday is missing.

Numbers of men and women who gave positive feedback

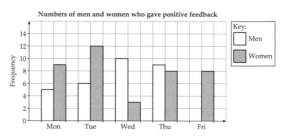

Key:
☐ Men
▨ Women

(a) How many women gave positive feedback on Tuesday?

Look at the height of the grey column on Tuesday. Be careful of the scale on the vertical axis.

12 ✔
(1)

Dianne knows that over the whole week the total number of men who gave positive feedback was the same as the total number of women.

(b) How many men gave positive feedback on Friday?

$9 + 12 + 3 + 8 + 8 = 40$ ✔
$5 + 6 + 10 + 9 = 30$ ✔
$40 - 30 = 10$ ✔

Follow these steps:
• work out the total number of women
• work out the total number of men for Mon, Tue, Wed and Thu
• subtract this from the total number of women.

10 ✔
(4)
(Total for Question 11 is 5 marks)

70

71

72

73

12 The table shows some information on how Tom spends his wages.

Item	Percentage of wages spent
Food	21%
Clothing	8%
Rent	41%
Entertainment	..15..% ✔
Other	15%

(a) Complete the table.

$21 + 8 + 41 + 15 = 85$

$100 - 85 = 15$ ✔

> The percentages must add up to 100%.

(2)

Last month Tom's wages were £1550

(b) How much of his wages did he spend on rent?

$\frac{41}{100} = 0.41$

$1550 \times 0.41 = 635.5$ ✔

> You need to find 41% of £1550. You could also divide by 100 then multiply by 41.

> Give answers in pounds to 2 decimal places.

£.......635.50.... ✔

(2)

(Total for Question 12 is 4 marks)

13

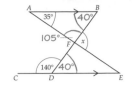

Diagram **NOT** drawn accurately

The lines AB and CE are parallel.
Angle BAF is 35°.
Angle CDF is 140°.

Work out the size of angle BFE, labelled x.

$180 - 140 = 40$ ✔

$\angle FDE = 40°$

> Angles on a straight line add up to 180°.

$\angle ABF = 40°$ ✔

> Alternate angles on parallel lines.

$180 - 35 - 40 = 105$ ✔

$\angle AFB = 105°$

> Angles in a triangle add up to 180°.

$180 - 105 = 75$

$x = 75°$

> Angles on a straight line add up to 180°.

.......75..... ✔ °

(Total for Question 13 is 4 marks)

14

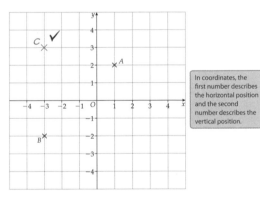

> In coordinates, the first number describes the horizontal position and the second number describes the vertical position.

(a) Write down the coordinates of the point A.

(....1...., ...2....) ✔

(1)

(b) Write down the coordinates of the point B.

(...−3..., ...−2...) ✔

(1)

(c) On the grid, plot the point $(−3, 3)$ with a cross ($\times$).
Label this point C.

(1)

(d) Write down the coordinates of the midpoint of AB.

$1 + -3 = -2$

$-2 \div 2 = -1$

> The x-coordinate of the midpoint is the mean of the two x-coordinates.

$2 + -2 = 0$

$0 \div 2 = 0$

> The y-coordinate of the midpoint is the mean of the two y-coordinates.

> You could also draw the line AB and find the midpoint by eye.

(...−1..., ...0...) ✔

(1)

(Total for Question 14 is 4 marks)

15 (a) Shade in **three** more squares on the diagram, to make a pattern with 1 line of symmetry.

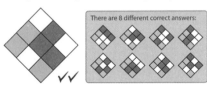

> There are 8 different correct answers:

✔✔

(2)

(b) Shade in **three** more squares on the diagram, to make a pattern with an order of rotational symmetry of 4

> The shape should fit over itself four times when rotated one full turn. You can use tracing paper to check your answer.

✔

(1)

(c) This large square is made from squares of different sizes.

What fraction of the large square is shaded?

> Be careful – don't just count squares because they're not all the same size. Draw lines to show all the small squares. The shape has an area of $5 \times 5 = 25$ small squares and 8 small squares are shaded.

.......$\frac{8}{25}$..... ✔✔

(2)

(Total for Question 15 is 5 marks)

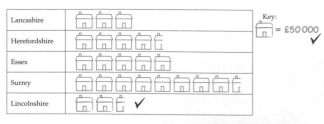

16 A magazine uses a pictogram to show the average house price in five different English counties.
The key for the pictogram is missing.

Lancashire	
Herefordshire	
Essex	
Surrey	
Lincolnshire	✔

Key:
🏠 = £50 000 ✔

The average house price in Herefordshire is £225 000

The average house price in Lincolnshire is £125 000

If 🏠 = £50 000 then 🏠 = £25 000

(a) Complete the pictogram to show this information.
Include a key for the pictogram.

225 000 ÷ 4.5 = 50 000 ✔
125 000 ÷ 50 000 = 2.5

4.5 houses represent £225 000, so each house represents £50 000.
Divide £125 000 by £50 000 to work out how many houses to draw for this row.

(3)

(b) Work out the average house price in Essex.

5 × 50 000 = 250 000
✔

There are 5 houses in the row for Essex, so multiply £50 000 by 5.

£ 250 000 ✔
(2)
(Total for Question 16 is 5 marks)

---

*17 David is shopping in a supermarket.
All of the items he buys are on special offer.

The table shows what he buys.

Item	Price each	Special offer	Number he buys
Loaf of bread	£1.25	Buy 2 for £2	2
Bag of dog food	£4.90	3 for the price of 2	3
Pizza	£2.40	Buy 1, get the 2nd for half price	2

What is the total amount of money that David saves by using the special offers?
You must show your working.

Bread
2 × 1.25 = 2.5
2.5 − 2 = 0.5 ✔
£0.50 saved

Work out how much he would have paid for 2 loaves of bread and subtract how much he actually paid.

Dog food
£4.90 saved ✔

He gets 1 bag of dog food free.

Pizza
2.4 ÷ 2 = 1.2 ✔
£1.20 saved

He saves half the cost of 1 pizza.

0.5 + 4.9 + 1.2 = 6.6
✔

Give answers in pounds to 2 decimal places.

£ 6.60 ✔
(Total for Question 17 is 5 marks)

---

18 (a) Solve x + 7 = 18

x = 18 − 7

Subtract 7 from both sides of the equation.

x = 11 ✔
(1)

(b) Solve 5y = 30

$y = \frac{30}{5}$

Divide both sides of the equation by 5.

y = 6 ✔
(1)

(c) Solve $\frac{x}{3} = 9$

x = 9 × 3

Multiply both sides of the equation by 3.

x = 27 ✔
(1)

(d) Solve 4y − 6 = 10

4y = 10 + 6 ✔
4y = 16
$y = \frac{16}{4}$

You need to do two steps to get y on its own:
• add 6 to both sides of the equation
• divide both sides of the equation by 4.

y = 4 ✔
(2)
(Total for Question 18 is 5 marks)

---

19 The diagram shows a square and an equilateral triangle.

Diagram **NOT** drawn accurately

6 cm

The perimeter of the square is the same as the perimeter of the equilateral triangle.

Work out the length of one side of the equilateral triangle.

✔
4 × 6 = 24 ✔
24 ÷ 3 = 8
✔

The square has four equal sides so its perimeter is 4 × 6 = 24 cm. The equilateral triangle has three equal sides so each side is 24 ÷ 3 = 8 cm long.

8 ✔ cm
(Total for Question 19 is 4 marks)

20 Use your calculator to work out

(a) 13.4²

Either use the x^2 key or work out 13.4 × 13.4. Write down all the digits on your calculator display.

179.56 ✔
(1)

(b) $16.5 - \sqrt{17.64}$

16.5 − 4.2 = 12.3
✔

You can work this out in one go on your calculator. You might need to use the S⇔D key to get your answer as a decimal number.

12.3 ✔
(2)
(Total for Question 20 is 3 marks)

78

79

80

81

*21 A supermarket sells strawberries in boxes of two different sizes.

Which is the better value for money?
You must show your working.

400 g
400 ÷ 1.25 = 320 g/£ ✓

900 g
900 ÷ 2.95 = 305.0847... g/£ ✓

The 400 g box is better value. ✓

> Divide the weight of each box by the cost in pounds to work out how many grams of strawberries you get per pound (£) in each box. You get more strawberries per £ in the 400 g box, so it is better value for money.

(Total for Question 21 is 3 marks)

*22 Leslie has a holiday job in Spain.
She needs to drive from Murcia to Santander.

This chart gives the driving distances, in kilometres, between different cities in Spain.

Alicante				
429	Madrid			
82	407	Murcia		
875	452	840	Santander	
494	312	544	398	Zaragoza

Leslie knows that 5 miles is about the same as 8 km.
She will drive at an average speed of 50 mph.

How long will it take her to drive from Murcia to Santander?
You must show your working.
Give your answer in hours and minutes.

840 ÷ 8 = 105 ✓
105 × 5 = 525 miles ✓

> Read the distance off the table. Divide by 8 then multiply by 5 to convert it from km to miles.

$T = \dfrac{D}{S}$ ✓

$= \dfrac{525}{50}$ ✓

= 10.5 ✓

10 hours and 30 minutes ✓

> Write the formula triangle for speed. Cover up the value you want to find (*T*) to get the formula.

> It takes 10.5 hours. Convert this into hours and minutes.

(Total for Question 22 is 5 marks)

23

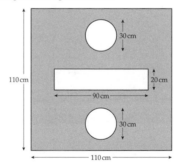

Diagram **NOT** drawn accurately

ABC is a right-angled triangle.
AB = 1.2 m.
BC = 3.5 m.

Calculate the length of *AC*.

> Use Pythagoras' theorem:
> $AB^2 + BC^2 = AC^2$

$AC^2 = 1.2^2 + 3.5^2$ ✓
$= 1.44 + 12.25$
$= 13.69$
$AC = \sqrt{13.69}$ ✓
$= 3.7$

> You don't need to round at any stage in this calculation.

> Check that your answer makes sense. You can't measure, but 3.7 looks about right and is longer than the other two sides.

3.7 ✓ m

(Total for Question 23 is 3 marks)

*24 The diagram shows a porch in the shape of a rectangle.

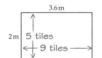

Diagram **NOT** drawn accurately

The porch is 3.6 m long and 2 m wide.

Dennis is going to cover the floor of the porch with square floor tiles.

Each floor tile is a square of side 40 cm.
Dennis buys 48 of the floor tiles.

Does Dennis buy enough floor tiles to cover the floor of the porch?
You must show all your working.

360 ÷ 40 = 9
200 ÷ 40 = 5 ✓
5 × 9 = 45 ✓
Yes ✓

> Convert all the lengths into the same units. Multiply metres by 100 to convert into cm.

> Work out how many tiles you can fit across the porch and how many you can fit up. Dennis needs 5 × 9 = 45 tiles in total and he has 48, so he does have enough.

(Total for Question 24 is 3 marks)

25 A perfume house is making two new fragrances.
Each bottle contains 350 ml.

'Sparkle' contains cedarwood and lavender in the ratio 2 : 5
'Shimmer' contains cedarwood and lavender in the ratio 5 : 12

Which fragrance, Sparkle or Shimmer, has the greater amount of cedarwood?
You must show your working.

Sparkle
2 + 5 = 7
350 ÷ 7 = 50
2 × 50 = 100 ✓

Shimmer
5 + 12 = 17
350 ÷ 17 = 20.5882...
5 × 20.5882 = 102.9411... ✓

> Work out the amount of cedarwood in each bottle. For Sparkle there are 2 + 5 = 7 parts in the ratio. So each part is worth 350 ÷ 7 = 50 ml. Multiply this by 2 to work out the amount of cedarwood.

> You could also write the amount of cedarwood in each bottle as a fraction, and compare the fractions.

Shimmer ✓

(Total for Question 25 is 3 marks)

*26 Miss Jebson makes an artwork for the wall of her school hall.

The artwork is made from a square panel of wood.
She cuts one rectangular hole and two circular holes out of the square panel of wood.

Each circle has a diameter of 30 cm.
The rectangle is 90 cm long and 20 cm wide.

Diagram **NOT** drawn accurately

Miss Jebson is going to paint the front of the artwork with one coat of paint.
One pot of paint covers 2500 cm².

How many pots of paint does Miss Jebson need?
You must show your working.

Square
110 × 110 = 12100

> Plan your answer, and write down all your working neatly.

Rectangle
90 × 20 = 1800 ✓

Circle
$\pi \times 15^2 = 225\pi$ ✓

> You can leave answers in terms of π until the end of the calculation.

$12100 - 1800 - 2 \times 225\pi = 8886.2833...$ ✓
$8886.2833... \div 2500 = 3.5545...$ ✓
4 pots ✓

> Miss Jebson must buy a whole number of pots, so she needs 4.

(Total for Question 26 is 5 marks)

TOTAL FOR PAPER IS 100 MARKS

1 (a)

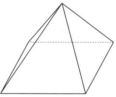

> There are 5 subdivisions between each thousand, so each one is worth 200.

Write down the number marked by the arrow.

3600 ✓

(1)

> There are 10 subdivisions between each ten, so each one is worth 1 unit.

(b)

Find the number −18 on the number scale.

Mark the number with an arrow (↑).

(1)

(c)

> There are 10 subdivisions between each 2 units, so each one is worth 0.2.

Write down the number marked by the arrow.

7.2 ✓

(1)

(Total for Question 1 is 3 marks)

2 The clocks show the time in London and in San Francisco.

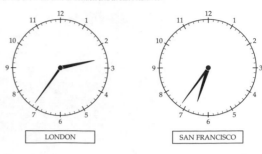

| LONDON | SAN FRANCISCO |

It is afternoon in London.

(a) Write down the time in London using the 24-hour clock.

> 2.36 pm = 14:36

14:36 ✓

(1)

It is morning in San Francisco when it is afternoon in London.

The time in London is ahead of the time in San Francisco.

(b) How many hours is London ahead of San Francisco?

> It is 6.36 am in San Francisco. You have to count on 8 hours to get to the time in London.

8 ✓ hours

(1)

(Total for Question 2 is 2 marks)

3 The diagram shows a square-based pyramid.

(a) How many faces does the shape have?

> Remember to count the faces you can't see.

5 ✓

(1)

(b) How many vertices does the shape have?

> Vertices is a mathematical word for corners.

5 ✓

(1)

(c) How many edges does the shape have?

8 ✓

(1)

(Total for Question 3 is 3 marks)

4

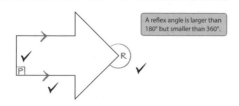

> A reflex angle is larger than 180° but smaller than 360°.

(a) Mark, with the letter P, a right angle.

(1)

(b) Mark, with the letter R, a reflex angle.

(1)

(c) Mark with arrows (>) two lines that are parallel.

(1)

(Total for Question 4 is 3 marks)

5 (a) Write down all of the common factors of 24 and 40

> The factors come in pairs:
> 1 × 24 = 24   2 × 12 = 24
> 3 × 8 = 24   4 × 6 = 24

Factors of 24: (1)(2) 3, (4) 6, (8) 12, 24

Factors of 40: (1)(2)(4) 5, (8) 10, 20, 40

1, 2, 4, 8 ✓ ✓

(2)

(b) Write down all of the prime numbers between 25 and 35

> 27 is not a prime number because 3 × 9 = 27.
> 33 is not a prime number because 3 × 11 = 33.

✓ ✓
29, 31

(2)

(Total for Question 5 is 4 marks)

6 On 27 February, Liam checks his bank statement for February so far.

Date	Details	Paid Out (£)	Paid In (£)	Balance (£)
				648.00
08/02/2013	South Electric	108.50		
18/02/2013	Trent Builders	745.00		
18/02/2013	MDM Insurance	13.50		
25/02/2013	Cheque 08829932		123.00	
26/02/2013	Top Nosh	53.00		

Liam started the month with £648.00 in his bank account.

How much does he need to pay in if he is to finish the month with £100 in his bank account? Show all of your working.

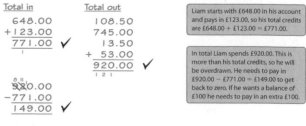

Total in
648.00
+123.00
771.00 ✓

Total out
108.50
745.00
13.50
+ 53.00
920.00 ✓

920.00
−771.00
149.00 ✓

> Liam starts with £648.00 in his account and pays in £123.00, so his total credits are £648.00 + £123.00 = £771.00.

> In total Liam spends £920.00. This is more than his total credits, so he will be overdrawn. He needs to pay in £920.00 − £771.00 = £149.00 to get back to zero. If he wants a balance of £100 he needs to pay in an extra £100.

149.00 + 100 = 249.00 ✓

£ 249.00 ✓

(Total for Question 6 is 5 marks)

7

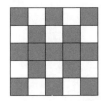

(a) What fraction of the shape is shaded?
Give your answer as a fraction in its simplest form.

$\frac{15}{25} = \frac{3}{5}$ ✔

> There are 15 shaded squares and 25 squares in total, so $\frac{15}{25}$ of the shape is shaded. Divide the numerator and denominator by 5 to simplify the fraction.

$\frac{3}{5}$ ✔

(2)

(b) (i) Write 17% as a fraction.

> You can write a percentage as a fraction with denominator 100.

$\frac{17}{100}$ ✔

(1)

(ii) Write your answer to (i) as a decimal.

$17 \div 100 = 0.17$

0.17 ✔

(1)

(Total for Question 7 is 4 marks)

8 Greta cut this shape from a 6 cm wide roll of cloth.
The shape is drawn on a centimetre grid.

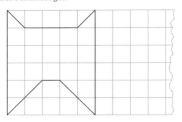

(a) Work out the area of the shape.

$17 + \frac{1}{2} \times 6 = 17 + 3 = 20$ ✔

> You can work this out by counting squares. There are 17 whole squares and 6 half squares.

20 ✔ cm²

(2)

The roll of cloth is 4 metres long.

(b) How many shapes could Greta cut from the roll?

$4\,m = 400\,cm$ ✔
$400 \div 5 = 80$ ✔

> Each shape is 5 cm long. Convert 4 m into cm, then divide by 5.

$40 \div 5 = 8$ so $400 \div 5 = 80$

80 ✔

(3)

(Total for Question 8 is 5 marks)

9 1 kg is about 2.2 pounds.

(a) Give an estimate for 15 kg in pounds.

$$\begin{array}{r} 15 \\ \times\ 22 \\ \hline 30 \\ 300 \\ \hline 330 \end{array}$$ ✔

> The question asks for an **estimate** so you could also write $15 \times 2 = 30$.

33 ✔ pounds

(2)

1 gallon is about 4.5 litres.

(b) Give an estimate for 36 litres in gallons.

$\frac{36}{4.5} = \frac{72}{9} = 8$ ✔

> The question asks for an **estimate** so you could also write $36 \div 4 = 9$.

8 ✔ gallons

(2)

(Total for Question 9 is 4 marks)

10 Nino carried out a survey about the exercise machines in some houses in his street.

He found there were 56 exercise machines altogether.

He started to draw this pictogram to show his results.

Key:
○ represents 8 machines

◯ represents 8 exercise machines

◖ represents 4 exercise machines

◿ represents 2 exercise machines

(a) How many rowing machines were there?

10 ✔

(1)

There were 16 exercise bikes.

(b) Show this information on the pictogram.

(1)

Nino found that there were twice as many steppers as treadmills.

(c) Complete the pictogram.

$56 - 10 - 16 = 30$ ✔
$30 \div 3 = 10$

> There were 56 exercise machines altogether. 30 of these were either steppers or treadmills, so divide 30 in the ratio 2 : 1.

Steppers
$2 \times 10 = 20$

Treadmills
$1 \times 10 = 10$

(2)

(Total for Question 10 is 4 marks)

11 Here are some patterns made from the letter B.

B   B B   B B B
B B   B B B   B B B B
Pattern 1   Pattern 2   Pattern 3

(a) Draw Pattern 4

B B B B
B B B B B ✔

> Each new pattern adds an extra column of Bs onto the left-hand side.

(1)

(b) Work out the number of times the letter B is used in Pattern 10

Pattern number	1	2	3	4	5	6	7	8	9	10
Number of Bs	3	5	7	9	11	13	15	17	19	21

✔

> Continue the sequence up to the 10th pattern.

21 ✔

(2)

(Total for Question 11 is 3 marks)

12 (a) Fill in 5 squares of the grid below.
Your shape must have exactly 4 lines of symmetry.

> You could also shade in these squares:

✔

(1)

(b) Fill in 5 squares of the grid below.
Your shape must have rotational symmetry of order 2

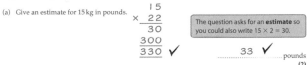

> The shape should fit over itself twice when rotated one full turn. You can use tracing paper to check your answer.

✔

(1)

(Total for Question 12 is 2 marks)

13 (a) Work out $7 - 4 \times 5 - 3$

$7 - 20 - 3 = -13 - 3 = -16$ ✔

> Remember BIDMAS – you work out Multiplication before Subtraction.

-16 ✔
(2)

(b) Write $4 \times 4 \times 4 \times 4 \times 4$ using index notation.

4^5 ✔
(1)

(c) Work out the value of $10^3 \div 5^2$

> Try and learn the cubes of 2, 3, 4, 5 and 10.

$1000 \div 25 = 40$ ✔

> $100 \div 25 = 4$ so $1000 \div 25 = 40$

40 ✔
(2)

(d) A candle burns down 0.8 cm every hour.

How long will it take to burn down 16 cm?

> Multiply the top and bottom of the division by 10.
> $16 \div 8 = 2$ so $160 \div 8 = 20$

$\dfrac{16}{0.8} = \dfrac{160}{8} = 20$ ✔

20 ✔ hours
(2)
(Total for Question 13 is 7 marks)

14 (a) Simplify $9m - m$

> m means '1 lot of m'.

$8m$ ✔
(1)

(b) Simplify $5k - 2p - 3k + 6p$

> $5k$ and $-3k$ are like terms and $-2p$ and $6p$ are like terms. Remember: each term goes with the sign ($+$ or $-$) in front of it.

$5k - 3k - 2p + 6p = 2k + 4p$ ✔

$2k + 4p$ ✔
(2)

(c) Solve $h - 11 = 12$

> Add 11 to both sides of the equation.

$h =$ 23 ✔
(1)

(d) Solve $3x - 4 = 17$

> Add 4 to both sides of the equation, then divide both sides of the equation by 3.

$3x = 21$ ✔
$x = 7$

$x =$ 7 ✔
(2)
(Total for Question 14 is 6 marks)

94

15 These letters are placed in a bag.

A letter is taken at random from the bag.

(a) Write down the probability that the letter is E.

> There are 2 letter Es and 7 letters in total.

$\dfrac{2}{7}$ ✔✔
(2)

(b) On the probability scale, mark with a cross (✗) the probability that the letter is A.

(1)

(c) Write down the probability that the letter is **not** E.

$1 - \dfrac{2}{7} = \dfrac{5}{7}$

> There are 5 letters which are not E.

$\dfrac{5}{7}$ ✔
(1)
(Total for Question 15 is 4 marks)

9

16 The diagram shows the numbers of goals scored by a hockey team over a season.

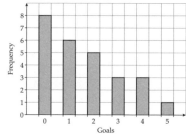

Fariq says that the team scored 3 or more goals just as often as they scored no goals.

Is he correct?
Give reasons for your answer.

> Work out the number of times the team scored 3 or more goals and compare that to the number of times they scored 0 goals. Show your calculation, and make sure you say 'yes' or 'no' to answer the question.

$3 + 3 + 1 = 7$ ✔

No. ✔ The team scored 0 goals 8 times and 3 or more goals

7 times. ✔

(Total for Question 16 is 3 marks)

96

*17

Diagram **NOT** drawn accurately

BCD and ACE are straight lines.
$AC = BC$.

Work out the size of angle x.
Give reasons for your answer.

$\angle BCA = 42°$ ✔

Vertically opposite angles are equal. ✔

> Write any angles you work out on the diagram, and remember to give reasons for each step of your working.

$\angle ABC = x$

Base angles in an isosceles triangle are equal.

$42° + x + x = 180°$
$2x = 138°$
$x = 69°$ ✔

Angles in a triangle add up to $180°$. ✔

> You can use a written method to work out $138 \div 2$:
> $2 \overline{)1\ 3\ ^1 8}$ $6\ 9$

(Total for Question 17 is 4 marks)

9

18 The diagram shows a cuboid.

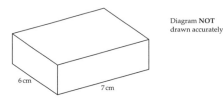

Diagram **NOT**
drawn accurately

6 cm

7 cm

The volume of the cuboid is 168 cm³.

Work out the height of the cuboid.

$$\begin{array}{r} 2\,8 \\ 6\overline{)1\,6\,{}^{4}8} \end{array}$$

$28 \div 7 = 4$
✓

> Volume of a cuboid = length × width × height.
> Divide the volume by the width, then divide the
> result by the length to work out the height.

........4........ ✓ cm

(Total for Question 18 is 2 marks)

19 Mr Sharp runs a cookery shop.

He wants to find out how often his customers eat meat.

He decides to give a questionnaire to 25 customers who spent £25 to £30 in his shop.

(a) Give one reason why his sample may be biased.

> You could also say that 25 is a small sample.

People who spend between £25 and £30 might not be typical
customers. ✓

(1)

(b) Write a suitable question for Mr Sharp's questionnaire.

How many times a week do you eat meat? ✓

> Your response boxes
> should cover all
> possibilities, and
> should not overlap.

☐ 0
☐ 1–2
☐ 3–4
☐ 5 or more ✓

(2)

(Total for Question 19 is 3 marks)

*20 These two card shops have special offers for Happy New Year cards.

> **Greetings**
> Happy New Year cards
> £1.66 each
> **3 for the price of 2**

> **For All Occasions**
> Happy New Year cards
> £1.35 each
> **Every 4th card free**

Melissa wants to buy 6 Happy New Year cards.

Melissa wants to buy the cards as cheaply as possible.
At which shop should she buy the cards?
Show all of your working.

> If you work in pence you don't need to do
> any calculations with decimal numbers.

Greetings

$$\begin{array}{r} 1\,6\,6 \\ \times\quad 4 \\ \hline 6\,6\,4 \\ \scriptstyle 2\,2 \end{array}$$

$4 \times 166 = 664$ ✓

For All Occasions

$$\begin{array}{r} 1\,3\,5 \\ \times\quad 5 \\ \hline 6\,7\,5 \\ \scriptstyle 1\,2 \end{array}$$

$5 \times 135 = 675$ ✓

> At Greetings Melissa gets 2 cards free.
> At For All Occasions she only gets 1 card
> free. Work out the costs at both shops
> then compare them.

At Greetings cards cost 664p and at For All Occasions cards
cost 675p. ✓

She should buy her cards at Greetings. ✓

(Total for Question 20 is 4 marks)

21 Four children each collected money for charity.
The pie chart below shows how much each of them collected.

Gary and Sharon collected the same amount.
Jensen collected £60

Work out how much Sharon collected.
Show all of your working.

$360 - 120 - 100 = 140$ ✓
$140 \div 2 = 70$ ✓
Sharon's angle = 70°

> There are 360° in a full circle. Use this to
> work out the angle of Sharon's sector.

120° represents £60
$60 \div 12 = 5$ ✓
So 10° represents £5

> You could divide by 120 to work out what 1°
> represents, but it's easier to divide by 12 to
> work out what 10° represents.

$5 \times 7 = 35$

£........35........ ✓

(Total for Question 21 is 4 marks)

22 Terri mixed 300 g of rice with 240 g of fish.

She added some onion to the mixture.

The ratio of the weight of fish to the weight of onion was 3 : 2

Work out the ratio of the weight of rice to the weight of onion.

$240 \div 3 = 80$ ✓
$2 \times 80 = 160$ ✓
Rice : Onion = 30̸0̸ : 16̸0̸ = 15 : 8

> 3 parts of the ratio represent 240 g so
> 1 part represents 80 g. Multiply 80 g by 2
> to work out the weight of onion in the
> dish. Then write the ratio of rice to onion
> and simplify it as much as possible.

........15 : 8........ ✓

(Total for Question 22 is 3 marks)

23 The diagram shows a heptagon.

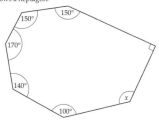

150° 150°

170°

140°

100°

x

Diagram **NOT**
drawn accurately

Work out the size of angle x.

$5 \times 180 = 900$ ✓

$$\begin{array}{r} 9\,0 \\ 1\,5\,0 \\ 1\,5\,0 \\ 1\,7\,0 \\ 1\,4\,0 \\ +\ 1\,0\,0 \\ \hline 8\,0\,0 \\ \scriptstyle 3 \end{array}$$ ✓

> The sum of the interior angles of an
> n-sided polygon is $(n - 2) \times 180°$.

$900 - 800 = 100$

........100........ ✓ °

(Total for Question 23 is 3 marks)

24 On the grid, draw the graph of $y = 2x + 3$ for values of x from -3 to 2

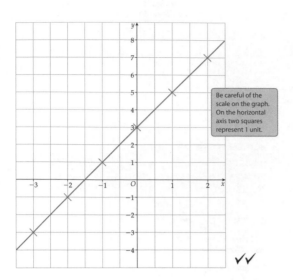

> Be careful of the scale on the graph. On the horizontal axis two squares represent 1 unit.

x	-3	-2	-1	0	1	2
y	-3	-1	1	3	5	7	✔

> You can also use $y = mx + c$ to draw the graph. $m = 2$ so the gradient of the graph is 2. $c = 3$ so the graph crosses the y-axis at $(0, 3)$.

> Use the equation $y = 2x + 3$ to work out at least 3 pairs of coordinates. For example, when $x = -3, y = 2 \times (-3) + 3 = -6 + 3 = -3$

(Total for Question 24 is 3 marks)

---

*25 These two rectangles have the same perimeter.

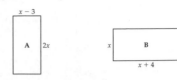

In the diagram, all of the measurements are in metres.

Work out the width and height of rectangle **A**.
Show all of your working.

Rectangle A
$$x - 3 + x - 3 + 2x + 2x = 6x - 6$$

> Work out expressions for the perimeter of each rectangle.

Rectangle B
$$x + x + x + 4 + x + 4 = 4x + 8$$

$$6x - 6 = 4x + 8 \quad ✔$$
$$6x = 4x + 14$$
$$2x = 14$$
$$x = 7 \quad ✔✔$$

> Write your expressions equal to each other to form an equation. Solve your equation to find x.

$$x - 3 = 7 - 3 = 4$$
$$2x = 2 \times 7 = 14$$

> Use x to work out the width and height of rectangle **A**. You need to show all of your working clearly.

width $= 4\,\text{m}$ ✔
height $= 14\,\text{m}$ ✔

(Total for Question 25 is 5 marks)

---

26 The scatter graph shows information about the number of people living in blocks of flats.
It shows the number of flats in a block and the total number of people living in the block.

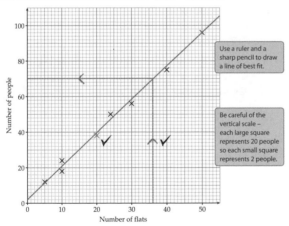

> Use a ruler and a sharp pencil to draw a line of best fit.

> Be careful of the vertical scale – each large square represents 20 people so each small square represents 2 people.

(a) What type of correlation does the scatter graph show?

Positive ✔

(1)

38 people live in another block of 20 flats.

(b) Plot this information on the graph.

(1)

(c) Estimate the number of people living in a block of 36 flats.

70 ✔

> Read up from 36 on the horizontal axis to your line of best fit, then read across to the vertical axis. Draw lines on your graph to show the values you are reading off.

(2)

(Total for Question 26 is 4 marks)

---

27 Three girls shared a full bottle of cola.

Karen drank $\frac{1}{4}$ of the bottle.

Rita drank $\frac{3}{10}$ of the bottle.

Megan drank the rest.

Work out the fraction of the bottle of cola which Megan drank.

$$\frac{1}{4} + \frac{3}{10} = \frac{5}{20} + \frac{6}{20} = \frac{11}{20} \quad ✔$$

$$1 - \frac{11}{20} = \frac{9}{20}$$
✔

> Add up the total amount Karen and Rita drank and subtract the total from 1.

$$\frac{9}{20}$$ ✔

(Total for Question 27 is 3 marks)

TOTAL FOR PAPER IS 100 MARKS

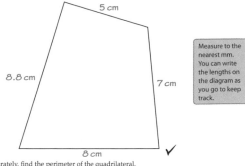

1 (a) Write the number 30 205 in words.

Thirty thousand two hundred and five ✔

Make sure you don't write any figures.

(1)

(b) Write down the value of the digit **3** in the number 2.3608

0.3 ✔

The 3 is in the tenths place. You could also write 3 tenths or $\frac{3}{10}$.

(1)

(c) Write down the number 3 020 536 to the nearest thousand.

3 021 000 ✔

Look at the digit in the hundreds place. It is 5 so round up.

(1)
(Total for Question 1 is 3 marks)

2

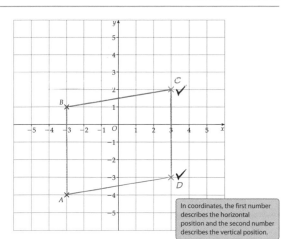

(a) Write down the coordinates of the point *A*.

In coordinates, the first number describes the horizontal position and the second number describes the vertical position.

(−3 , −4) ✔

(1)

(b) Plot the point *C* (3, 2) on the grid.

(1)

ABCD is a parallelogram.

(c) Mark the point *D* on the grid.

You can draw the parallelogram to check your answer.

(1)
(Total for Question 2 is 3 marks)

106

3 Here is a quadrilateral.

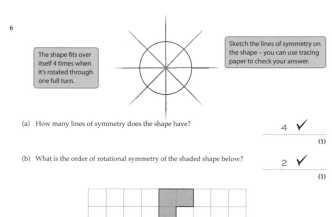

By measuring accurately, find the perimeter of the quadrilateral.

8.8 + 5 + 7 + 8 = 28.8 ✔

The perimeter is the distance all the way around a shape.

Measure to the nearest mm. You can write the lengths on the diagram as you go to keep track.

28.8 ✔ cm

(Total for Question 3 is 3 marks)

4 In a game, 5 players each put 12 counters on a table.

Sasha wins 35% of the counters.

Peter wins $\frac{2}{5}$ of the counters.

Haydon wins the remaining counters.

How many counters did Haydon win?
Show all of your working.

5 × 12 = 60 ✔

$\frac{35}{100}$ × 60 = 21 ✔

There were 5 × 12 counters in total. Work out how many counters Sasha and Peter win and subtract these from 60.

$\frac{2}{5}$ × 60 = 24 ✔

60 − 21 − 24 = 15

15 ✔

(Total for Question 4 is 4 marks)

107

5

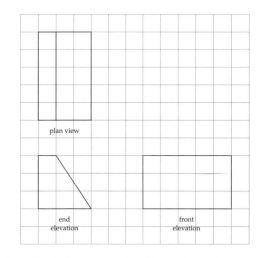

plan view

end elevation

front elevation

The diagram shows the plan view, end elevation and front elevation of a prism.
The diagram is drawn on a grid of centimetre squares.

Sketch the prism.
Show the dimensions on your diagram.

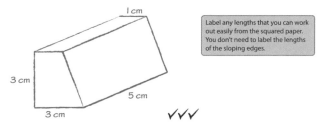

Label any lengths that you can work out easily from the squared paper. You don't need to label the lengths of the sloping edges.

1 cm

3 cm

5 cm

3 cm ✔✔✔

(Total for Question 5 is 3 marks)

108

6

The shape fits over itself 4 times when it's rotated through one full turn.

Sketch the lines of symmetry on the shape – you can use tracing paper to check your answer.

(a) How many lines of symmetry does the shape have?

4 ✔

(1)

(b) What is the order of rotational symmetry of the shaded shape below?

2 ✔

(1)

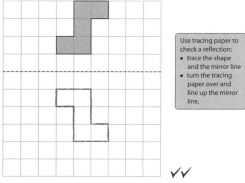

Use tracing paper to check a reflection:
• trace the shape and the mirror line
• turn the tracing paper over and line up the mirror line.

✔✔

(c) Reflect the shaded shape in the dotted line.

(2)
(Total for Question 6 is 4 marks)

109

153

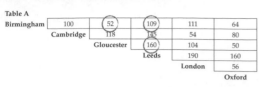

7 Table A show the distances, in miles, between some towns.

Table A

Birmingham	100	(52)	(109)	111	64
	Cambridge	118	145	54	80
		Gloucester	(160)	104	50
			Leeds	190	160
				London	56
					Oxford

Table B shows the cost of delivering a parcel the same day by a courier service.

Table B

		Distance (miles) up to			
		50	100	150	200
Weight up to	5 kg	£42	(£56)	£64	£91
	10 kg	£51	£72	£83	£126
	20 kg	£58	£87	(£99)	£152
	50 kg	£90	£121	£144	(£215)

Ramon has businesses in Birmingham, Gloucester and Leeds.

Work out the total cost for Ramon to send the following parcels.

2 kg parcel from Birmingham to Gloucester   52 miles, £56 ✓✓

43 kg from Gloucester to Leeds   160 miles, £215

12 kg parcel from Leeds to Birmingham   109 miles, £99

56 + 215 + 99 = 370 ✓

> Use the weight and the distance to work out the cost of each parcel. It is 52 miles from Birmingham to Gloucester. This means it is in the 'up to 100 miles' category.

£ ....370....... ✓

(Total for Question 7 is 4 marks)

110

---

*8 These conversion graphs can be used to convert between Pounds (£), Dollars ($) and Euros (€).

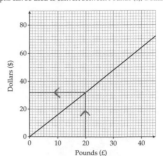

> Draw lines on the graphs to show the values you are reading off. Always read graphs correct to the nearest small square.

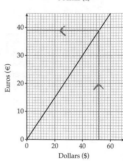

Warren has $20 and £20

Can he afford a radio that costs €45?

£20 = $32 ✓

32 + 20 = 52 ✓

$52 = €39

No. He only has €39 and he needs €45. ✓

> Follow these steps:
> • convert £20 into $
> • add on the $20 Warren already has
> • convert the total into €
> • compare the result with €45 and write a conclusion.

(Total for Question 8 is 3 marks)

1

---

*9 In a café, some people ordered the following types of coffee.

	Americano	Latte	Cappuccino	Espresso
Men	12	18	30	20
Women	6	28	36	16

Draw a suitable diagram to show the information in the table.
Use the grid below.

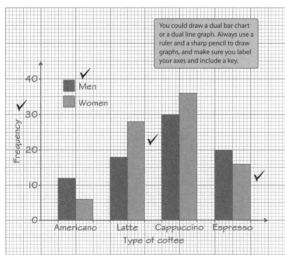

> You could draw a dual bar chart or a dual line graph. Always use a ruler and a sharp pencil to draw graphs, and make sure you label your axes and include a key.

(Total for Question 9 is 4 marks)

112

---

10 Paula has saved £17.88 using 2p, 5p and 10p coins.

There are 464 coins altogether.
$\frac{1}{4}$ of the coins are 5p coins.
£6.40 is in 10p coins.
The rest of the coins are 2p coins

Work out the number of 2p coins.
Show all your working.

5p coins
464 ÷ 4 = 116 ✓

> There are 116 five pence coins and 64 ten pence coins.

10p coins
£6.40 = 640p
640 ÷ 10 = 64 ✓

> Work in pence or pounds, but not both. To work out how many 10p coins there are, convert £6.40 into 640p then divide by 10.

2p coins
464 − 116 − 64 = 284 ✓

> You could check your answer using the total amount:
> 116 × 5 + 64 × 10 + 284 × 2 = 1788 ✓

.......284....... ✓

(Total for Question 10 is 4 marks)

1

11 Clarissa wants to put two coats of paint on the walls of her lounge.

The walls have a total area of 47 m².

A 2 litre tin of paint costs £6.99
2 litres of paint cover an area of 24 m².

How much will it cost for Clarissa to paint the walls of her lounge?

2 × 47 = 94

94 ÷ 24 = 3.916... ✔

4 tins of paint needed ✔

4 × £6.99 = £27.96
　　　✔

> Clarissa wants to paint two coats, so in total she has to paint an area of 2 × 47 = 94 m².

> Clarissa has to buy a whole number of tins.

£ ....27.96...... ✔
(Total for Question 11 is 4 marks)

12 Here are the instructions for cooking a piece of meat.

> 25 minutes per 500 g plus 30 minutes extra

The meat weighs 2.5 kg.

Work out the time needed to cook the meat.

2.5 kg = 2500 g ✔

2500 ÷ 500 = 5

25 × 5 = 125 ✔

125 + 30 = 155
　　　✔

> The formula uses grams, so convert 2.5 kg into 2500 g. Divide by 500 to work out how many lots of 500 g this is.
> Remember to add the 30 minutes extra.

.........155...... ✔ minutes
(Total for Question 12 is 4 marks)

13 Here is a list of numbers.

> Write the values in order of size. Cross each value off the list as you write it.

5̶1̶ 4̶8̶ 2̶ 5̶3̶ 5̶0̶ 4̶8̶ 1̶ 5̶2̶ 5̶5̶ 4̶9̶

(a) Work out the median.

1, 2, 48, 48, (49, 50), 51, 52, 53, 55 ✔

> There are 10 data values. The median is half way between the 5th and 6th values.

49.5 ✔
(2)

(b) Work out the mean.

51 + 48 + 2 + 53 + 50 + 48 + 1 + 52 + 55 + 49 = 409

409 ÷ 10 = 40.9
　　　✔

> Add together all the data values and divide by the number of data values.

40.9 ✔
(2)

(c) Work out the range.

> Range = largest value − smallest value

55 − 1 = 54

54 ✔
(1)
(Total for Question 13 is 5 marks)

14

Diagram **NOT** drawn accurately

(a) Why is it impossible for angle x to be 238°?

> $x + 90° + 22° = 360°$, so angle x is equal to $360° − 90° − 22° = 248°$.

90 + 22 + 238 = 350

Angles around a point should add up to 360°. ✔
(1)

(b)

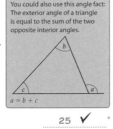

Diagram **NOT** drawn accurately

BCD is a straight line.
BEC is a triangle.
Angle DCE = 163°.
Angle EBD = 138°.

Work out the size of the angle x.

> Remember to write down any angle facts you use.

180 − 163 = 17 ✔

Angles on a straight line add up to 180°.
　　　✔

180 − 17 − 138 = 25

$x = 25°$

Angles in a triangle add up to 180°.

> You could also use this angle fact: The exterior angle of a triangle is equal to the sum of the two opposite interior angles.
> $a = b + c$

.........25...... ✔ °
(3)
(Total for Question 14 is 4 marks)

15 (a) (i) Write down √60
Show all the figures on your calculator display.

> You might need to use the [S⇔D] key to get your answer as a decimal number.

7.745966692 ✔
(1)

(ii) Give your answer to (i) correct to 2 decimal places.

> Look at the digit in the third decimal place. It is 5 so round up.

7.75 ✔
(1)

(b) Calculate the exact value of $2.6^3 − 1.2^4$

17.576 − 2.0736 = 15.5024
　　　✔

> You could enter this into your calculator in one go using the [x▯] key on your calculator.

15.5024 ✔
(2)
(Total for Question 15 is 4 marks)

16 Write these numbers in order of size, from smallest to largest.

0.63　58%　$\frac{3}{5}$

58% = 0.58

$\frac{3}{5}$ = 3 ÷ 5 = 0.6 ✔

0.58, 0.6, 0.63

> You could also convert all three numbers into percentages to compare them:
> • 0.63 = 63%
> • $\frac{1}{5}$ = 20% so $\frac{3}{5}$ = 60%

> Write the original values in order of size.

58%, $\frac{3}{5}$, 0.63 ✔
(Total for Question 16 is 2 marks)

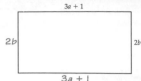

17

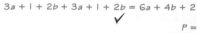

$3a + 1$

$2b$ $2b$

$3a + 1$

Diagram **NOT** drawn accurately

In the diagram, all measurements are in centimetres.

> Follow these steps:
> • write expressions for the other two sides on the diagram
> • add together the expressions for all four sides
> • simplify by collecting like terms.

(a) Write a formula for the perimeter, P cm, of this rectangle.

$3a + 1 + 2b + 3a + 1 + 2b = 6a + 4b + 2$ ✓

$P = 6a + 4b + 2$ ✓ ✓

....

(3)

(b) Work out the perimeter of the rectangle when $a = 5.5$ and $b = 0.4$

$6 \times 5.5 + 4 \times 0.4 + 2 = 36.6$ ✓

> You have to do multiplication before addition.
> If you enter the calculation into your calculator accurately then it will use the correct order of operations.

36.6 ✓ ..... cm

(2)

(Total for Question 17 is 5 marks)

18 The three faces of a spinner are numbered 1, 2 and 3

The table shows the results of spinning the spinner 120 times.

Number	Frequency
1	61
2	22
3	37

> If the spinner was fair then each number would come up about $120 \div 3 = 40$ times. Compare the frequencies with 40 and write a conclusion.

Do you think the spinner is biased?
Explain your answer.

$120 \div 3 = 40$

Yes, because the frequencies for 1 and 2 are not close to 40. ✓

(Total for Question 18 is 1 mark)

19 Leandro asked 45 people if they are on Twitter or Facebook or neither.
The table shows his results.

Neither	Twitter	Facebook
10	25	30

Work out the number of people who are on both Twitter and Facebook.

$10 + 25 + 30 = 65$

$65 - 45 = 20$ ✓

> Add up the three values. If no-one was on both Twitter and Facebook there would be 20 too many people, so 20 people must have been counted twice.

20 ✓

(Total for Question 19 is 2 marks)

20 An aeroplane travels 805 miles at a speed of 575 mph.

How long does the journey take?
Give your answer in minutes.

> Draw the formula triangle for speed.

$T = \dfrac{D}{S}$

$805 \div 575 = 1.4$ ✓

> Distance is in miles and speed is in mph so time will be in hours. Multiply by 60 to convert it into minutes.

$1.4 \times 60 = 84$ ✓

84 ✓ ..... minutes

(Total for Question 20 is 3 marks)

21 The diagram shows two types of plastic building block.

A   B

←— 24 mm —→   ←— 32 mm —→

Diagram **NOT** drawn accurately

Block A is 24 mm long.
Block B is 32 mm long.

Jeremy joins some type A blocks together make a straight row.
He then joins some type B blocks together to make a straight row of the same length.

Write down the shortest possible length of this row.

Multiples of 24: 24, 48, 72, (96) ...

Multiples of 32: 32, 64, (96) ... ✓

> The length of the row of type **A** blocks must be a multiple of 24, and the length of the row of type **B** blocks must be a multiple of 32. The shortest possible length is the lowest common multiple (LCM) of 24 and 32.

96 ✓ ..... mm

(Total for Question 21 is 2 marks)

22 Alec asked a group of people how many text messages they sent yesterday.
The table shows the results.

Number	Frequency f	Midpoint x	$f \times x$
0–4	38	2	76
5–9	24	7	168
10–14	22	12	264
15–19	15	17	255
20–24	15	22	330
Total	114		1093

✓ ✓

> Add columns to your table for 'Midpoint' and 'Frequency × Midpoint'. Add a row to your table for the Total frequency and the sum of the $f \times x$ column.

Work out an estimate for the mean of the data.

$1093 \div 114 = 9.5877...$ ✓

> Estimate of the mean $= \dfrac{\text{Sum of } f \times x \text{ column}}{\text{Total frequency}}$

> Write down at least 4 decimal places of your calculator display before rounding your answer to 1 d.p.

9.6 ✓

(Total for Question 22 is 4 marks)

23 The equation

$$\frac{x^2}{1 + x} = 2$$

has a solution between 2 and 3

Use a trial improvement method to find this solution.
Give your answer correct to 1 decimal place.
You must show all your working.

x	$\dfrac{x^2}{1 + x}$	Too big or too small?
2.5	1.7857...	Too small ✓
2.7	1.9702...	Too small
2.8	2.0631...	Too big
2.75	2.0166...	Too big ✓ ✓

> Work out $\dfrac{x^2}{1 + x}$ for different values of x between 2 and 3. Use a table like this to keep track of your working.

> You need to try $x = 2.75$ to check whether x is closer to 2.7 or 2.8.

$x = 2.7$ ✓

(Total for Question 23 is 4 marks)

24 (a) Factorise $12m - 16n$

> Look for the largest factor you can take out of both terms in the expression.

$4(3m - 4n)$ ✓

(1)

(b) Factorise completely $10m^2 - 5m$

> $5(2m^2 - m)$ and $m(10m - 5)$ are both only partly factorised.

$5m(2m - 1)$ ✓

(2)

(Total for Question 24 is 3 marks)

25 The diagram shows the position of a surveyor, *S*, and Disneyland, *D*.

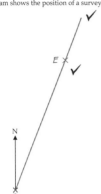

×*D*

E ×

N

×
S

> Use a protractor to draw a line on a bearing of 21° from S. Remember to measure clockwise from North, and try to be accurate to the nearest degree.

> Use a ruler to draw a cross 8 cm along your line, accurate to the nearest mm.

The surveyor can see the Eiffel Tower 32 km away on a bearing of 021°.

(a) Using a scale of 1 cm to 4 km, mark the position of the Eiffel Tower with the letter *E*.

$32 \div 4 = 8$

(2)

(b) How far is the surveyor from Disneyland?

> The distance is 14.5 cm on the scale drawing. Multiply by 4 to get the real-life distance in km.

$14.5 \times 4 = 58$ ✔

.... 58 ✔ .... km

(2)

(Total for Question 25 is 4 marks)

122

---

26 Taahir weighs each potato in a bag.
These are his results.

200g 221g 184g 199g 223g
190g 190g 186g 206g 219g
186g 205g 206g 192g 198g

> Cross off each value as you enter it in your stem and leaf diagram.

(a) Complete the stem and leaf diagram for the data.

18	4 6 6
19	0 0 2 8 9 ✔
20	0 5 6 6
21	9
22	1 3 ✔

Key:
18 | 4 represents 184 g ✔

> Remember to include a key, and check that you have written 15 'leaves'.

(3)

Taahir finds another potato in the bag that weighs 220 g.

(b) Has the range of weights changed?
Give a reason for your answer.

No, because 220 g is not the largest or the smallest value. ✔

(1)

(Total for Question 26 is 4 marks)

123

---

27 Liz stood next to her dog Jock.

She threw a stick 40 metres away from them.

Jock took 8 seconds to reach the stick, running at a constant speed.

He spent 2 seconds picking up the stick.

Jock ran back to Liz at a constant speed of 4 m/s.

Use the grid below to draw a distance–time graph.

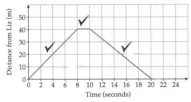

> You need to work out how long it takes Jock to run back to Liz. Draw the formula triangle for speed:
> Time = $\frac{\text{Distance}}{\text{Speed}}$

$T = \frac{D}{S} = \frac{40}{4} = 10$

(Total for Question 27 is 3 marks)

124

28

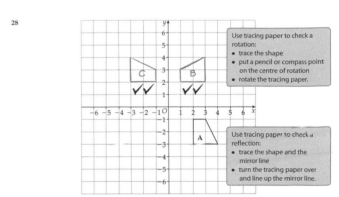

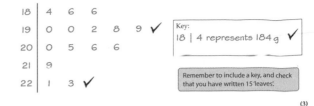

> Use tracing paper to check a rotation:
> - trace the shape
> - put a pencil or compass point on the centre of rotation
> - rotate the tracing paper.

> Use tracing paper to check a reflection:
> - trace the shape and the mirror line
> - turn the tracing paper over and line up the mirror line.

(a) Rotate shape **A** 90° anti-clockwise about the origin (0, 0).
Label the image **B**.

(2)

(b) Reflect the shape **B** in the line with equation $x = 0$
Label the image **C**.

> The line $x = 0$ is another name for the y-axis.

(2)

(Total for Question 28 is 4 marks)

125

157

Diagram **NOT**
drawn accurately

C

12 mm

A   30 mm   *B*

The diagram shows a right-angled triangle *ABC*.

Work out the length of *AC*.
Give your answer correct to 1 decimal place.

$AC^2 = 30^2 - 12^2 = 900 - 144$ ✓
$\qquad\qquad\qquad = 756$

$AC = \sqrt{756} = 27.4954...$
✓

> Check that your answer makes sense. The diagram is not drawn accurately so you can't measure, but it should look about right. *AC* must be shorter than *AB*.

> *AC* is one of the shorter sides of the triangle.
> $AC^2 + BC^2 = AB^2$, so
> $AC^2 = AB^2 - BC^2$

<u>27.5</u> ✓ mm
(Total for Question 29 is 3 marks)

TOTAL FOR PAPER IS 100 MARKS